PO

by
R. A. PENFOLD

BERNARD BABANI (publishing) LTD
THE GRAMPIANS
SHEPHERDS BUSH ROAD
LONDON W6 7NF
ENGLAND

Please Note

Although every care has been taken with the production of this book to ensure that any projects, designs, modifications and/or programs, etc., contained herewith, operate in a correct and safe manner and also that any components specified are normally available in Great Britain, the Publishers do not accept responsibility in any way for the failure (including fault in design) of any project, design, modification or program to work correctly or to cause damage to any other equipment that it may be connected to or used in conjunction with, or in respect of any other damage or injury that may be so caused, nor do the Publishers accept responsibility in any way for the failure to obtain specified components.

Notice is also given that if equipment that is still under warranty is modified in any way or used or connected with home-built equipment then that warranty may be void.

© 1980 BERNARD BABANI (publishing) LTD

First Published – August 1980
Reprinted – September 1983
Reprinted – September 1985
Reprinted – July 1986
Reprinted – October 1987
Reprinted – July 1988
Reprinted – August 1989
Reprinted – September 1990
Reprinted – January 1993
Reprinted – July 1994
Reprinted – June 1996
Reprinted – March 1999
Reprinted – June 2003

British Library Cataloguing in Publication Data
Penfold, R. A.
    Power supply projects.
    1. Electronic apparatus and appliances – Power supply
    2. Electronics – Amateurs' manuals
    I. Title
    621.381'044   TK9965
    ISBN 0 900162 96 1

Printed and bound in Great Britain by Antony Rowe Ltd, Chippenham, Wiltshire

CONTENTS

INTRODUCTION

Every item of electronic equipment requires a power supply of some kind. Probably the majority of home-constructed electronic equipment is these days powered from batteries, and with modern semiconductor-based circuits battery operation is quite feasible even for some highly complex items of electronic equipment. However, there are numerous circuits where battery operation would not be a practical proposition; one would not, for example, contemplate powering a high power amplifier from a battery supply. Even with low power equipment, battery operation is more expensive in the medium and long term than using a mains power supply.

Mains power supplies then, are an essential part of many electronic projects, and increasingly used in low power circuits in preference to batteries. The purpose of this book is to give a number of power supply designs, including simple unstabilised types, fixed voltage regulated types, and variable voltage stabilised designs, the latter being primarily intended for use as bench supplies for the electronics workshop. Apart from giving a number of designs which will satisfy most requirements, the information provided should help the reader to design his or her own power supply circuits, using components that are to hand, or those that are available at low cost. The designs provided are all low voltage types for semiconductor circuits. Valves are so rarely used in new designs that high voltage supplies have been omitted, although the principles outlined for low voltage unregulated supplies apply to unregulated high voltage supplies as well.

There are other types of power supply apart from the a.c. mains to low voltage d.c. type, and a number of these are dealt with in the final chapter, including a car-cassette power supply, Ni-Cad battery charger, d.c. voltage step up circuit, and a simple inverter.

CHAPTER 1

POWER SUPPLIES

Unregulated Supplies

An unregulated mains power supply consists of three basic sections; a transformer to step down the mains voltage to the required level and to provide safety isolation, a rectifier to convert the a.c. output of the transformer to a form of d.c., and a smoothing circuit to change the rough or pulsating d.c. from the rectifier to a reasonably smooth and ripple-free d.c.

The most simple form of power supply is the half wave unregulated type, and this uses the basic arrangement shown in Figure 1. The mains input is applied to the primary winding of the mains transformer, and a low voltage a.c. output is extracted from its secondary. There is no direct connection between the mains supply and the secondary circuit of T1, and it is therefore perfectly safe to come into electrical contact with the secondary circuit of T1, provided, of course, that the transformer has an output voltage that is fairly low. Some transistor circuits, such as power amplifiers, use transformers having secondary voltages of about 40 to 60 volts, and these

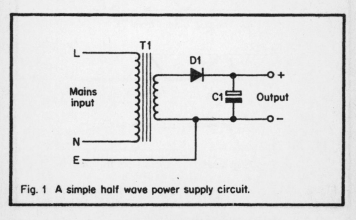

Fig. 1 A simple half wave power supply circuit.

3

are capable of inflicting a mild electric shock, but under normal circumstances are not dangerous. The secondary circuit of T1 is connected to the mains earth connection so that if by some means the mains supply should become connected to this side of T1, there will be a large current flow to earth, blowing the mains fuse and cutting off the mains supply. This also reduces the risk of anyone touching the secondary circuit getting a shock to earth of any severity in the brief period before the fuse blows.

The output from T1 is taken by way of rectifier D1, and this is only conductive when the lower connection of T1's secondary is negative, and the upper connection is positive. On opposite half cycles D1 blocks any significant current flow. Thus the a.c. input to D1 has the waveform of Figure 2(a), and the output is d.c., having the waveform of Figure 2(b). This rough or pulsating signal is obviously not suitable to power most electronic circuits. Not only does the supply voltage vary very considerably and rapidly, it is also totally absent for 50% of the time!

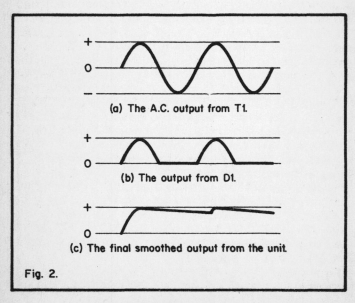

(a) The A.C. output from T1.

(b) The output from D1.

(c) The final smoothed output from the unit.

Fig. 2.

This problem is partly overcome by the addition of smoothing capacitor C1. A capacitor has the ability to store an electrical charge, and so on the first positive going half cycles the output rises much as before, charging up C1 to the peak positive output voltage from T1. Then, as the output voltage from T1 starts to fall away, the charge on C1 provides the output current, and continues to do so until the output voltage from T1 returns to virtually its peak positive value once again. C1 is then 'topped up' once again, and provides the output current as the voltage from T1 drops away, until the next peak positive pulse from T1. It should be noted that T1 only provides an output and charging current for the brief periods during which the voltage provided by T1 is higher than the charge voltage on C1. For the remainder of the time D1 is reverse biased and does not conduct. This assumes D1 to be a theoretically perfect component with zero forward resistance, which it is not, and it should perhaps be pointed out that for a normal silicon rectifier there will be a forward voltage drop of about 0.5 volts. Therefore, in actual fact D1 only conducts when the voltage from T1 is about 0.5 volts more than the charge voltage on C1, and the output voltage is approximately 0.5 volts less than the peak output voltage from T1.

As C1 cannot have an infinite value, it cannot provide a perfectly smooth d.c. output. There must be some drop in the output voltage during the comparatively long intervals between the charging pulses from T1. This gives an output waveform of Figure 2(c), which is a form of sawtooth waveform. The variation in the output voltage due to the inadequacies of the smoothing circuit is normally called the 'ripple content', or just 'ripple'. What constitutes an acceptable amount of ripple depends very much on the characteristics of the equipment being fed by the supply. Some logic circuits and audio amplifiers are capable of operating from supplies giving ripple levels of several hundred millivolts or even more, since they are designed to have an inherently high level of ripple rejection. Other circuits will malfunction or give an unacceptably high background level of mains hum if there is even a millivolt or two of ripple on the supply lines.

In general, unregulated supplies are only used where a fair

amount of ripple can be tolerated, as an excessively large smoothing capacitor would be needed in order to give a really low ripple content on the output, even if only modest currents were to be drawn from the unit.

Full Wave Rectification

In practice it is unusual for a simple half wave circuit such as that shown in Figure 1 to be used, probably because it is rather inefficient. This is due to the mains transformer only providing a brief output pulse once during each cycle, and a transformer having a low secondary impedance is needed in order to give a sufficiently large pulse of current. Another disadvantage of half wave rectification is the relatively long period between charging pulses from the transformer, necessitating the use of a comparatively large smoothing capacitor.

The second of these problems can be overcome by using a full wave circuit of the type shown in Figure 3. This requires a mains transformer having a centre tapped secondary winding, or two identical secondaries connected in series to give the same effect. The two halves of the secondary are in effect fed to separate half wave rectifying circuits of the type previously described, with the two outputs being connected together and smoothed by a common smoothing capacitor.

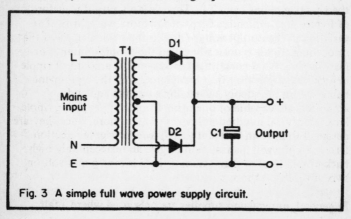

Fig. 3 A simple full wave power supply circuit.

6

Although this may at first seem to give two half wave circuits connected in parallel, and giving no advantage over a single half wave circuit, this is not in fact the case. The two rectifiers operate in a push-pull arrangement, since when the upper section of the secondary is providing a positive-going signal, the lower one is providing a negative-going one, and vice versa. Thus, on one half cycle D1 provides the charging pulse to C1. On the next half cycle D2 provides the charging pulse to C1, and this process continues with D1 and D2 feeding C1 with charging pulses on alternate half cycles.

This type of circuit is no more efficient than a simple half wave type, because although C1 is now charged twice per cycle, and T1 only has to give half the current required by a halfwave circuit during each charging pulse, this is nullified by the fact that either two secondaries or a larger centre tapped secondary is required. Thus, where a half wave circuit might use (say) a 12 volt 250 mA transformer, a full wave circuit of this type would need to use a $12 - 0 - 12$ volt 125 mA component, or one having two 12 volt 125 mA secondaries. In either case the transformer for the full wave circuit has a power rating of 3 watts in total, which is precisely the same as the half wave circuit.

The advantage of this type of rectifier is that it requires a smoothing capacitor of only about half the value of that used in an equivalent half wave circuit for a similar level of smoothing. This is simply because the smoothing capacitor receives a 'topping up' charge twice as frequently in a full wave circuit as it does in a half wave one. The capacitor therefore only has to provide about half as much power between charges in a full wave circuit, and therefore only needs to have about half the value needed in a half wave circuit in order to give the same level of smoothing.

Figure 4 shows the output waveforms from various parts of the circuit of Figure 3. Note that whereas the frequency of the ripple on the output was the same as the input frequency for the half wave circuit (50 Hz nominal for the U.K. mains), the ripple is at double the input frequency in the case of the full wave circuit. This is not of any great practical significance,

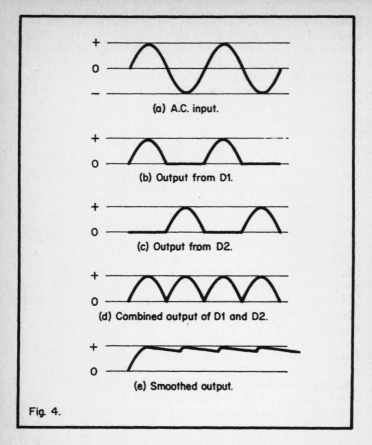

+
0
−

(a) A.C. input.

+
0

(b) Output from D1.

+
0

(c) Output from D2.

+
0

(d) Combined output of D1 and D2.

+
0

(e) Smoothed output.

Fig. 4.

although in audio circuits the 50 Hz hum of a half wave supply is slightly less noticeable than the 100 Hz hum of a full wave type. This is more than compensated for by easier smoothing of a full wave supply though, and in practical circuits a half wave supply is not often used, except where high ripple content is not of great importance and only a low output power is required, making efficiency unimportant.

Bridge Rectifier

A bridge rectifier is a full wave type that does not need a centre tapped secondary winding on the mains transformer, and just needs a single untapped secondary as used for a half wave circuit. Since this single winding provides two charging pulses to the smoothing capacitor per cycle, it is much more efficient than the two forms of rectification considered previously.

Figure 5 shows the basic circuit of a full wave bridge rectifier power supply. As can be seen from this, a bridge rectifier uses a ring of four diodes, and these dirct the output of the transformer in such a way as to always give a positive going output signal.

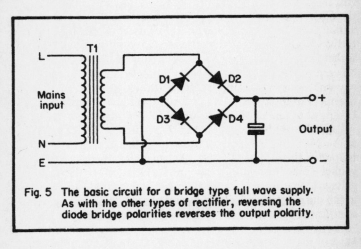

Fig. 5 The basic circuit for a bridge type full wave supply. As with the other types of rectifier, reversing the diode bridge polarities reverses the output polarity.

For example, when the lower connection of T1 is negative and the upper connection is positive, the output current (using conventional current flow from positive to negative) flows through D2, the load connected across the output, and then D3. When the polarity of the output from T1 is reversed, the current flows through D4, the load connected across the output, and then through D1.

9

Thus, in effect, the connections to T1 are reversed at the beginning of each half cycle, so that the polarity of the output does not change, and full wave rectification is provided.

Drawbacks

The obvious advantage and attraction of an unregulated supply is its simplicity and attendant low cost, but there are several drawbacks to supplies of this type. One of these is that a high value smoothing capacitor is needed in order to obtain a really well smoothed output. Another is that wide variations in the output voltage can, and in most applications do, occur.

One might think that variations in the mains supply voltage that inevitably occur are primarily responsible for changes in the output potential. However, this is not really the case, although such changes do obviously contribute to some extent to the variations. Since the mains supply is normally much higher than the output voltage of the supply, the voltage step down provided by the mains transformer similarly steps down any variations in the supply voltage at the output of the circuit. For instance, a 12 volt supply will suffer a change in output potential of only 120 mV (0.12 volts) if the mains voltage changes by 2.4 volts. In other words, a 10% change in the 240V mains supply causes a 10% change in the 12 volt output of the supply. Very large changes in the mains supply voltage do not normally occur, and so variations in the input voltage are unlikely to cause any really substantial variation in the output voltage. Certainly not enough to be of any significance with most items of electronic equipment.

Most of the variation in output potential of an unstabilised supply is due to loading of the supply. There is a certain amount of resistance in the secondary winding of the mains transformer, and through the rectifier circuit. If a current is drawn from the supply, a voltage is developed across the secondary winding, and the voltage drop through the rectifier circuit increases slightly. The total of these voltages is subtracted from the output voltage of the circuit, and can cause an extremely large reduction in output voltage.

10

If we take a simple example, a mains transformer used in a circuit of the type shown in Figure 3, and having a secondary rating of 12 − 0 − 12 volts at 1 amp., would probably give an unloaded output voltage of about 1.5 times its nominal secondary potential, or approximately 18 volts in other words. Steadily increasing the loading on the output up to 1 amp would cause the output voltage to gradually reduce to something in the region of 11 to 13 volts. Reducing the loading from zero to maximum thus gives a drop in the output voltage of about 33 1/3%!

Most items of electronic equipment consume a varying amount of current, and when used with an unregulated supply produce large variations in the supply voltage. This can often produce problems with feedback through the supply lines. Another problem is that an item of equipment such as a class B power amplifier might need a supply voltage of (say) 24 volts at maximum load, but be only able to withstand a maximum supply voltage of about 30 volts without sustaining damage. This would be a difficult piece of equipment to operate from an unstabilised supply because a 24 volt transformer having the appropriate secondary current rating would give a satisfactory loaded supply voltage, but would give a supply potential of probably about 35 or 36 volts under quiescent conditions. This would be far too high to apply to the amplifier. A 20 volt transformer would give a safe quiescent voltage of only about 29 or 30 volts, but the fully loaded supply voltage would only be about 20 volts (assuming the transformer has a current rating equal to the maximum load current). A 20 volt transformer having a secondary current rating of double or more the required maximum output current would give satisfactory results, but with the added expense and bulk of a suitable transformer, one might as well use a stabilised supply.

Another example of where an unstabilised supply would probably be unsuitable is as a battery eliminator for a transistor radio. Here the problem would be that a transformer giving a suitable fully loaded supply voltage would tend to give a rather high supply potential under quiescent or low load conditions. While the set would probably not be damaged by the unloaded supply voltage, it would probably result in the mixer and

I.F. stages of the set becoming rather lively, giving rise to strong spurious responses or even instability. Again, a transformer having a high secondary current rating could be used, but a stabilised supply would be a more sensible choice.

One other drawback of unstabilised supplies is that the unloaded and loaded supply voltages are rather hard to predict. In theory, a transformer having a secondary voltage of 12 volts r.m.s., for example, would give a peak output voltage of 1.41 times the r.m.s. output voltage, or just under 17 volts in this case. The final unloaded d.c. output potential would be about 1 volt less than this if a bridge rectifier were used, due to the voltage drop across the rectifiers (assuming silicon devices are used). However, most 12 volt transformers on the market today actually give an unloaded d.c. output of about 18 volts, some 2 volts higher than one would expect. One 12 volt transformer in the author's spares box was tested and found to give an unloaded d.c. output of some 20 volts, about 25% more than one might expect.

While there are many circuits where wide variations in the supply voltage are of no consequence, and neither is the precise supply potential, this is obviously not always the case. It is therefore necessary to carefully consider the situation before deciding to use an unstabilised supply for an item of equipment.

Choosing Components

It is quite an easy matter to choose the appropriate components for an unstabilised supply of a particular loaded output voltage and current.

If we first consider a circuit of the type shown in Figure 3, the mains transformer should have a voltage rating equal to, or fractionally more than the required loaded d.c. output voltage. Its current rating should be at least as high as the required maximum output current. If the transformer has a current rating which is well in excess of the required maximum output current, the low loading of the transformer will almost certainly result in the output voltage under maximum load being about 10 to 20% more than required. Therefore, apart from considerations of cost and bulk, it is not advisable to use a transformer that has a current rating well in excess of what is really necessary, unless its voltage rating is suitably lowered.

The two rectifiers should have a current rating at least equal to the maximum output current of the supply, and their p.i.v. (peak inverse voltage) rating should be no less than three times the voltage rating of the transformer (which is approximately double the unloaded output voltage of the supply). This may seem to be unnecessarily high at first sight, but it must be remembered that the cathode of each diode connects to the output, and is at the positive supply rail voltage. The anode connection varies from fractionally above the positive rail voltage to a negative voltage of equal amplitude. When the circuit is in the latter state, the cathode of the rectifier is positive by an amount equal to the positive rail voltage, while the anode is negative of the negative supply rail by an almost equal amount. There is thus a reverse voltage of approximately double the supply voltage across the rectifier.

The voltage rating of the smoothing capacitor must be at least 1.5 times the voltage rating of the transformer, and its capacitance value should be at least 1 μF per mA of output current in order to obtain a well smoothed output, and should preferably be several μF per mA of supply current.

A parameter which is sometimes quoted for capacitors, and which is of relevance here, is the maximum ripple current. Although in theory a capacitor can charge and discharge at a rate only limited by the charging circuit, like any other component, practical capacitors can only handle a finite amount of current. The smoothing capacitor must have a ripple current rating which is at least as high as the maximum output current of the power supply.

Choosing a mains transformer for a power supply incorporating a bridge rectifier is not quite as straightforward as choosing one for a push-pull type circuit. In theory, the maximum current that should be drawn from the transformer when employing a bridge rectifier is 0.62 of the a.c. current rating of the transformer. However, in practice it is quite common for the maximum d.c. output of a power supply to be equal to the current rating of the transformer, as will become apparent when looking at a few practical published designs. In an application where there is to be a continuous and high current consumption from the supply, it would probably be as well to be on the safe side and use a transformer which has a current rating of 1.5 times (or more) the required output current. In applications where a high output current only occurs intermittently, or the equipment is not used for prolonged periods, there are unlikely to be any problems if the current rating of the transformer is equal to or little more than the required maximum output current.

The voltage rating of the mains transformer is chosen in the same way as for the push-pull rectifier circuit. The rectifiers and smoothing capacitors are also selected in the same way.

The use of half wave supplies is not really recommended, except perhaps where very low output current is required, as the low efficiency of these circuits means that the maximum output current available is only a little more than a quarter of the a.c. current rating of the transformer (usually somewhat more in practice). Also, the smoothing capacitor must have a value of double that which would be required in an equivalent full wave circuit.

Rectifier Ratings

The table given below shows the two basic ratings for some popular rectifiers, and should aid the choice of suitable types for readers own power supply designs.

p.i.v.	1 amp max. average forward current	3 amp max. average forward current
50	1N4001	1N5400
100	1N4002	1N5401
200	1N4003	1N5402
400	1N4004	1N5404

600	1N4005	1N5406
800	1N4006	1N5407
1,000	1N4007	1N5408

If we now take a couple of simple examples of choosing components for unregulated supplies; a 12 volt supply having a maximum load current of 500 mA could use a 12 − 0 − 12 volt mains transformer having a 500 mA secondary current rating, together with a push-pull rectifier circuit. The peak inverse voltage across the rectifiers will be about three times the transformer voltage, or approximately 36 volts in other words. In the above table the 1N4001 is the smallest (and cheapest) rectifier capable of handling a p.i.v. of more than 36 volts and an average forward current of over 500 mA, and is the obvious choice. The smoothing capacitor needs a value of about 1 μF per mA of output current, and so a 470 μF component is the smallest that is likely to give satisfactory results. If the powered circuit is something like an audio amplifier which is not likely to be tolerant of ripple on the supply lines, a higher value of 1,000 μF or 2,200 μF would be advisable. The unloaded output voltage of the supply is likely to be about 18 volts or so, and so the capacitor must have a voltage rating of at least this figure, a 25 volt type being the lowest suitable voltage rating that is likely to be available in practice. Of course, a high voltage component, such as a 40 volt one, could be used if it is to hand, provided it is not physically too large to fit into the proposed layout.

For our second example, let us assume that a 19 volt supply providing a maximum load current of 240 mA is required, and that a full wave, bridge type rectifier is to be used. It is unlikely that a 19 volt transformer will be available, and so either an 18 or 20 volt type must be used. If the supply is to supply the maximum 240 mA load current for prolonged periods it would probably be better to use an 18 volt type having a secondary current rating of about 400 to 500 mA.

The fact that the transformer is not used at anything like its maximum current rating ensures that it will not be overloaded, and overheating of the component will be avoided. The low loading also helps to compensate for the low voltage rating of the transformer, and the d.c. output voltage should be close to the required 19 volts.

If the supply will only need to supply the full 240 mA output current intermittently, and 18 volt 250 mA transformer (or a 9 − 0 − 9 volt 250 mA type with the centre tap ignored) should give satisfactory results, although the d.c. output voltage might be fractionally low at maximum loading. A 20 volt 250 mA type should also be suitable, although in this case the output potential will be slightly higher than required. However, both types should give results of adequate accuracy since an unstabilised supply is not suitable for applications where the supply voltage is critical.

The rectifiers must withstand a peak inverse voltage of about 54 (18 x 3) or 60 (20 x 3) volts, at a maximum average current of 240 mA, and so four 1N4002 types would be suitable. The smoothing capacitor requires a value of about 240 μF, 220 μF being the nearest preferred value to this. For applications where a really well smoothed supply is needed a 470 μF or 1,000 μF component should be used. The capacitor will be subjected to a maximum voltage of about 27 (18 x 1.5) or 30 (20 x 1.5) volts, and 40 volts is the lowest suitable working voltage in which capacitors are commonly available.

Series — Parallel Transformers

There are a number of transformers available these days which have twin secondaries of idential voltage and current ratings. These are designed so that they can be used with the windings connected in series or in parallel. For example, a transformer having two 12 volt 500 mA secondary windings can be connected as shown in Figure 6(a) in order to give a 24 volt 500 mA output. This is the series mode. By using the junction of the two windings, the component can be used as a 12 − 0 − 12 volt 500 mA type, as shown in Figure 6(b).

With the windings connected in parallel, as shown in Figure 6(c), the transformer is effectively a 12 volt 1 amp type. In other words, series operation gives double the output voltage

16

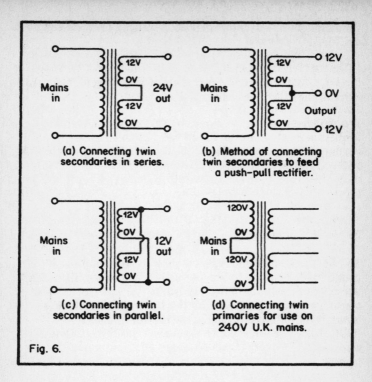

(a) Connecting twin secondaries in series.

(b) Method of connecting twin secondaries to feed a push–pull rectifier.

(c) Connecting twin secondaries in parallel.

(d) Connecting twin primaries for use on 240V U.K. mains.

Fig. 6.

of a single winding, and parallel operation gives twice the output current of a single winding. When using the parallel mode it is necessary to make quite sure that the windings are connected correctly, since a very high current will flow if the connections to one of them is reversed, causing the component to quickly burn out.

For the same reason it is also important that the parallel mode should only be used if the manufacturers or retailers literature states that the two secondary windings are accurately matched, and can be safely used in the parallel mode. With types not specifically designed for parallel operation there is a real risk that there will be a small but significant difference in the two secondary voltages. This would result in one winding forcing a fairly heavy current through the other

17

winding, causing the component to eventually overheat and be destroyed.

Of course, it is not essential to use both windings of a transformer, and if one winding is capable of supplying the required current, the other one can simply be ignored.

It is perhaps worth mentioning here that some of the transformers available these days have two 120 volt primary windings. These can be connected in parallel for use on the 120 volt (or thereabouts) mains supply found in many countries, or in series for use on the 240 volt U.K. mains supply (see Figure 6(d)).

Improved Smoothing

The smoothing of a simple power supply can be improved considerably by using two smoothing capacitors together with a resistor or choke, as shown in Figures 7(a) and 7(b) respectively. One problem with this method is that there is inevitably a voltage drop across the resistor or choke, necessitating the use of a higher voltage transformer. In the case of the choke, there are the added disadvantages of the rather high cost and large size of a suitable component. This type of smoothing circuit is not often used these days because it is probably better to use a simple stabilised circuit (which provides electronic smoothing).

Fusing

Although mains plugs containing fuses are in common use these days, the lowest current rating commonly available for these plugs is 3 amps. This is far higher than the current consumption of most items of electronic equipment, and affords little protection. It may therefore be worthwhile adding a fuse in the 'live' mains lead to the mains transformer. For reasons of safety it is advisable to fit it in a panel mounting fuseholder, and not a chassis mounting type (where there would be a strong risk of an electric shock being sustained if

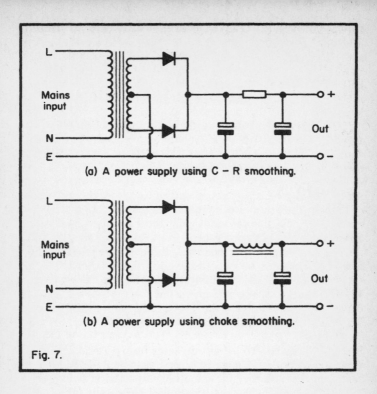

(a) A power supply using C – R smoothing.

(b) A power supply using choke smoothing.

Fig. 7.

the fuse was to be changed while the equipment was still plugged into the mains).

In order to find the current rating for the fuse, first multiply the secondary current taken from the transformer by its secondary voltage, so as to determine the power drawn from it. For instance, if 250 mA is drawn from a 12 volt transformer, the maximum power taken from the supply is 12V x 0.25A = 3 watts. If 2 amps current is drawn from a 20 – 0 – 20 volt transformer, the output power is 20V x 2A = 40 watts. If the transformer has more than one secondary, the output powers of the secondaries must be added together to derive the total power drawn from the transformer. The total output power in watts is then divided by the mains voltage (240V in the U.K.) to give the primary current. Thus, in our two examples above, the primary currents are 12.5 mA and 166 mA respectively. To allow for losses through the transformer a further 50% should be added, giving 18 mA and 250 mA in the above examples. A 100 mA fuse would probably have to be used in the first case, since this is the lowest fuse rating that is generally available. In the second case a 250 mA fuse can be used, as this is a rating in which fuses are readily available. If the calculated rating does not coincide with one that is available, always choose the nearest rating that is higher than the calculated one.

A fuse can also be added in one output lead from the secondary of the transformer, and will protect the transformer in the event of a smoothing capacitor going short circuit, a fault in the rectifier circuitry, or a general overload on the supply. In the case of a transformer feeding a push-pull type rectifier, the fuse is connected in series with the lead from the centre tap on the secondary (i.e. the 0V connection). The fuse has a rating which is equal to the maximum output current that will be drawn from the supply, or the lowest rating above this figure if a fuse of the appropriate rating is not available.

It may be necessary to use an anti-surge fuse, particularly if a very large smoothing capacitor is used, as the initial and high charge current taken by the smoothing capacitor at switch-on can often be sufficient to activate 'quick blow' type fuses.

CHAPTER 2

FIXED VOLTAGE REGULATED SUPPLIES

There are many applications where the variations in supply
voltage associated with unstabilised supplies would result in
the equipment giving inconsistent results, or where damage
could even be inflicted on the supplied equipment, as explained
in the previous chapter. There are also a number of
applications where a very well smoothed supply is required,
and a stabilised supply is of advantage here because the
regulator circuit counteracts all variations in the output
potential, including ripple.

In this chapter we shall be concerned with stabilised supplies
that provide a single voltage, and are primarily intended for use
as a permanent part of some larger piece of equipment. Variable
voltage stabilised supplies, primarily intended for use as bench
power supplies, will be dealt with in the subsequent chapter.

Zener Stabilisation

The most simple form of voltage regulator is the zener shunt
stabiliser, and this uses the very simple circuit shown in
Figure 8. The zener diode has a voltage rating which is equal
to the required output voltage, or the nearest preferred value
to the desired voltage if there is no preferred value giving the
correct voltage.

At voltages below its rated voltage a zener diode has a very
high resistance, usually many megohms. If the applied
voltage is taken above the rated voltage, or 'zener voltage' as it
is more commonly known, the resistance of the device drops
considerably. In fact, raising the applied voltage to only a
fraction of a volt above the zener voltage may well cause the
effective resistance of the device to fall to just a few ohms.

The input voltage must, of course, be somewhat higher than

21

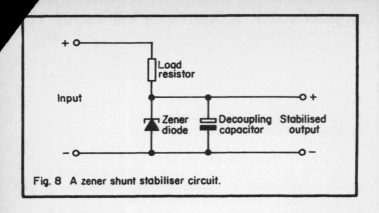

Fig. 8 A zener shunt stabiliser circuit.

the stabilised output voltage. The zener diode then 'avalanches' into conduction, causing a voltage drop across the load resistor and producing an output voltage approximately equal to its zener voltage. Increasing the input voltage causes the zener diode to conduct more heavily, causing a higher current to flow and the voltage dropped across the load resistor to increase. This results in the output voltage only marginally increasing. Conversely, if the input voltage decreases, the zener diode conducts less heavily, a lower current flow is produced, and the voltage drop across the load resistor decreases. This gives only a marginal drop in the output voltage.

The circuit not only guards against variations in the input potential, but prevents output loading (within reason) from producing large variations in the output voltage. For example, if there is an increase in the output current, this tends to reduce the output voltage, and the zener conducts less heavily. Thus, although the increased output current raises the voltage drop across the load resistor, this is largely offset by the zener conducting less heavily, and only a slight reduction in the output voltage actually occurs.

One problem with a zener diode is that when used in this way it tends to generate a certain amount of noise, and it does so over a very wide bandwidth. In fact zener diodes are sometimes employed in noise generators. This will not always be of any importance, but in many applications it is necessary to add a decoupling capacitor across the zener in order to severely attenuate this noise. In mains power supplies the addition of this capacitor, together with the load resistor, gives additional smoothing. The stabilisation effect of the zener diode also gives smoothing of the supply.

Low Voltage Zeners

Most zener diodes give excellent regulation performance in practice, but the performance of most lower voltage types is usually markedly inferior to the high voltage components. It is devices having voltage ratings below about 6.2 volts that have a lower level of performance, as can be seen by referring to the two graphs shown in Figure 9. These show the zener voltage versus zener current for a 3.9V and a 8.2V device. As can be seen from these, the voltage across the 8.2V type does not vary a great deal, and increases in proportion to the zener current producing a straight line on the graph. The response for the 3.9V type is reasonably flat at zener currents of about

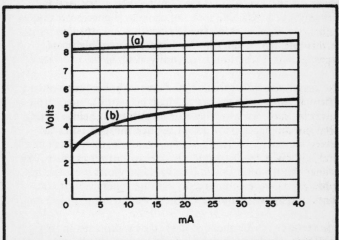

Fig. 9 Peformance curves for (a) a typical 8·2V zener, and
(b) a typical 3·9V type.

25 to 40 mA, but is very steep at currents of between zero and a few mA, giving very mediocre performance.

Therefore, in highly critical applications it is better *not* to use a low voltage zener, unless only fairly small variations in the zener current are likely to occur.

Zener Ratings

There are three principal ratings for zener diodes; zener voltage, the error tolerance of the zener voltage, and the maximum permissible power dissipation.

As the zener voltage does vary somewhat with the current flowing through the device, it must be given at some particular current. For the popular BZY88 series of zeners, for instance, the zener voltage is specified at a current of 5 mA. Naturally the zener voltage will not be precisely the specified figure, and for the BZY88 series of devices it will be within 5% of the rated voltage (at a zener current of 5 mA). The maximum power dissipation figure is really self explanatory, and is 400 mW for the BZY88 series of zeners. Higher power types such as the BZX61 series (which have a 1.3 watt maximum permissible dissipation) are available, but very high power types seem to be no longer generally available.

The reason for this is that zener shunt stabilisers are not very efficient, since there is always a high current drain on the power source even when little or no current is being drawn from the supply. In low power applications, whether the power source is a battery or a mains transformer, efficiency is rarely of any great consequence. In high power circuits a zener shunt stabiliser can lead to rather short battery life in battery powered equipment, and the generation of unnecessarily large amounts of heat whatever the power source.

It is therefore recommended that the use of zener shunt stabilisers should be restricted to low power applications. For higher power circuits it is usually better to use a series regulator, and these will be covered later in this chapter.

Zener Polarity

The zener diode must be connected with the polarity shown in Figure 8 if it is to function correctly. If the input and output supply polarities are reversed, then the polarity of the zener must also be reversed (as must the polarity of the decoupling capacitor) for the circuit to operate properly. If the zener is connected the wrong way around it is then merely an ordinary forward biased silicon diode, and effectively produces a zener voltage of about 0.7 volts (actually fractionally more than most silicon diodes).

The fact that a forward biased silicon diode acts as a very low voltage zener can, and often is, put to good use. Zener diodes having voltages below about 2.7 volts are not generally available, and so some alternative is needed for lower voltages. A forward biased silicon diode, or several in series is a simple and inexpensive method of obtaining very low stabilised potentials.

For example, if a stabilised supply of 2 volts is needed, the basic circuit configuration of Figure 10 can be used. Here there are three silicon diodes in series which effectively form a zener diode. There is about 0.65 volts developed across each diode, giving a total zener voltage of approximately 1.95 volts. This should be close enough to the required figure of 2 volts for the majority of applications.

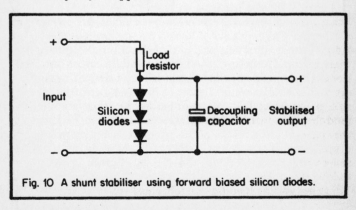

Fig. 10 A shunt stabiliser using forward biased silicon diodes.

25

Amplified Diode

Another form of low voltage regulator is the 'amplified diode' arrangement shown in Figure 11. If we assume that R1 and R2 have the same value, the circuit will provide a zener voltage of about 1.2 or 1.3 volts. This is because about 0.6 to 0.65 volts is required at the base of Tr1 in order to switch the device on, and a marginally higher voltage is all that is needed in order to bias the device hard into conduction. The voltage at the output therefore rises to about 1.2 or 1.3 volts, whereupon Tr1 conducts heavily and prevents any significant further rise in voltage. The circuit thus provides an effect which is similar to a zener diode.

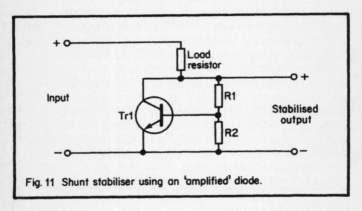

Fig. 11 Shunt stabiliser using an 'amplified' diode.

However, one important property of this form of regulator is that within reason, any desired output voltage can be obtained. For example, reducing the value of R2 increases the voltage drop across the potential divider circuit, and increases the voltage needed at Tr1's collector before the device switches on (and therefore increases the effective zener voltage). Decreasing the value of R1 has the opposite effect, reducing the voltage drop through the potential divider and decreasing the effective zener voltage of the circuit.

The zener voltage is approximately equal to:—

$$0.65 \, (R1 + R2)/R2$$

An important asset of this configuration is that the potential divider can be formed by a preset potentiometer, and the output voltage is then adjustable from about 0.65 volts up to about 6 volts or so. The performance of the circuit falls off as the output voltage increases, due to the decreased level of feedback caused by increased losses through the potential divider. It is therefore not advisable to use this configuration for voltages of more than about 6 volts.

For best results a high gain transistor should be used, such as a BC109C, BC169C, BC650 or similar. A p.n.p. device can be used, but the input polarity must be reversed. R1 and R2 should not be so high in value that they do not provide a reasonably large base current for Tr1, but not be so low as to prevent an adequate output voltage being obtained by producing an excessive voltage drop across the load resistor. The total resistance through the load resistor is usually about ten times the load resistance value.

The performance of silicon diode stabilisers and amplified diode regulators is normally very good, and superior to that obtained from low voltage zener diodes. One slight problem is that the temperature stability of these circuits is not quite as good as can be attained using a zener diode. However, the voltage change from silicon diodes and amplified diodes is only about 0.3 to 0.4% per degree Centigrade, and is not a problem in the majority of applications.

Load Resistor Value

Whatever form of shunt regulator is used, the load resistor must have a low enough resistance to provide the required output current when the input voltage is at its minimum level. For example, if a 5.6 volt zener is fed from a 9 volt battery supply, and a maximum output current of 10 mA is required, a load resistor of 190 ohms in value is required. This is because the output voltage from a 9 volt battery that is nearing exhaustion but is still in a useable state is only about 7.5 volts, and with

5.6 volts across the zener this only leaves about 1.9 volts across the load resistor. From Ohm's Law we know that resistance equals voltage divided by current, which gives us 1.9 volts divided by 0.01 amps (10 mA), which equals 190 ohms.

To allow for component tolerances a slightly lower value would be used in practice, say 180 ohms or perferably 150 ohms.

With a new battery connected to the circuit there will be a supply voltage of about 9.5 volts, giving about 3.9 volts across the load resistor and a current flow of 22 mA (180 ohm load resistor) or 26 mA (150 ohm load resistor). The power dissipation in the zener diode is therefore only about 145.6 mW (5.6 volts x 0.026 amps = 0.1456 watts or 145 mW) even with the lower load resistor value, and so a small zener such as a BZY88C5V6 400 mW type is perfectly suitable.

The maximum power dissipation in the load resistor is only about 101.4 mW (3.9 volts x 0.026A = 0.1014 watts or 101.4 mW) even if it has the lower value of 150 ohms, and so even a miniature 1/8 watt type could be used here, although it would be advisable to use a more conservatively rated component in the interests of long term reliability.

Series Regulators

A series regulator is one where the input current is little higher than the output current, the difference between the two currents being the small amount drawn by the regulator itself. In effect, a series regulator is a variable resistance connected into one supply rail, with the resistance automatically adjusting itself to whatever value is needed in order to maintain the output voltage at the appropriate level. Its main advantage over a shunt type regulator is its high efficiency, resulting in a minimum of wasted power and heat generation. For this reason, series regulators are normally used in all applications, except where very low powers are involved, and efficiency and heat generation are not of any great importance.

In its simplest form a series regulator can merely consist of a
zener shunt regulator feeding an emitter follower buffer stage,
as shown in Figure 12. There is unity voltage gain through an
emitter follower stage, and so by applying a stabilised input to
the base, a stabilised output is obtained from the emitter. As
the transistor provides current gain, the output current from
the emitter can be far higher than the input current to the
base. Thus, with a current flow of about 1 or 2 mA in the zener
shunt stabiliser circuit, and a quiescent current consumption of
the same level of course, an output current of perhaps 100 mA
or more would be available at the output. The input current is
equal to the output current plus the 1 or 2 mA drawn by the
zener stabiliser, and so quite good efficiency is attained.

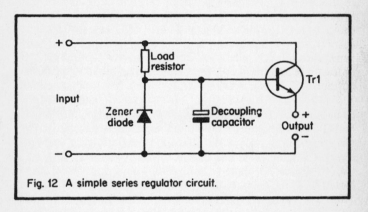

Fig. 12 A simple series regulator circuit.

Provided the input voltage to the circuit is not inadequate to
give the desired output voltage, the voltage at the output is
virtually independent of the input voltage, and is controlled
by the base voltage of Tr1. The zener diode and decoupling
capacitor produce a very well smoothed voltage at Tr1's base,
and this is reflected in an output which is almost equally free
from noise. This enables circuits of this type to produce
outputs having very low ripple and noise contents without the
use of especially large smoothing capacitors, even at output
currents as high as 1 amp or more. Output noise levels of
about 1 mV maximum are quite typical for power supplies of
this general type, and noise levels of just a few tens of

29

microvolts can be readily attained.

The output voltage from a circuit of this type is not equal to the
zener voltage, since there is a voltage drop of about 0.65 volts
between the base and emitter terminals of Tr1. This drop
must therefore be subtracted from the zener voltage in order
to give the nominal output voltage of the circuit. This voltage
drop assumes that the output impedance of the emitter
follower stage is very low in comparison to the load impedance.
In other words, the current in the zener stabiliser circuits
multiplied by the current gain of the transistor should give an
answer that is far higher than the maximum output current.
The regulation of this type of circuit can never be equal to the
regulation of the zener circuit, since the emitter follower
cannot have zero output impedance, and the voltage drop
through the stage must increase slightly with increasing output
current. However, good regulation will be obtained if the
zener current multiplied by the current gain of the transistor is
at least one hundred times the required maximum output
current.

In practice this usually means that two or even three transistors
must be used in order to obtain sufficient gain. A basic two
transistor circuit using an emitter follower Darlington pair is
shown in Figure 13(a) and Figure 13(b) shows the method of
using three transistors in a Darlington − emitter follower circuit.
Note that using two transistors results in an increased voltage
drop of about 1.3 volts from the base of the first transistor to the
output, since approximately 0.65 volts is dropped across each
transistor. For a three transistor circuit this means a voltage
drop of just under 2 volts from the base of the first transistor
to the output.

An arrangement which is occasionally encountered is one where
two common emitter amplifiers with 100% overall negative
feedback are used. This arrangement is shown in Figure 14.
Although common emitter stages normally have a high level of
voltage gain, this is not the case here due to the 100% negative
feedback which is applied from the collector of the output
transistor to the emitter of the driver transistor. This gives the
amplifier a gain of almost exactly unity.

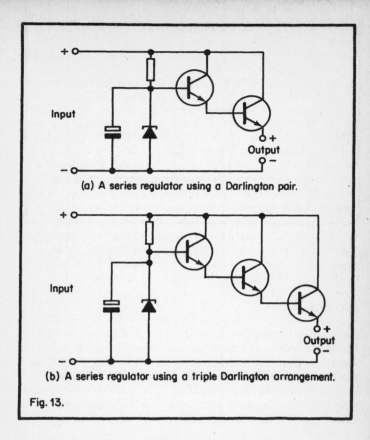

(a) A series regulator using a Darlington pair.

(b) A series regulator using a triple Darlington arrangement.

Fig. 13.

An advantage of this arrangement over a Darlington Pair emitter follower circuit is its lower voltage drop from the input to the output. The voltage drop through this type of circuit is only about 0.65 volts, permitting higher efficiency, and enabling the circuit to function properly even if the unstabilised input voltage is only a few hundred millivolts higher than the required output voltage.

All the configurations shown in Figures 12 to 14 can be made to operate with a positive earth rail, but the polarity of the zener must be reversed, n.p.n. transistors should be changed to

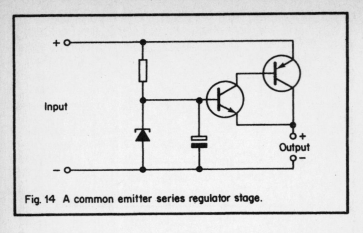

Fig. 14 A common emitter series regulator stage.

p.n.p. types, and p.n.p. devices should be altered to n.p.n. types.

Battery Eliminator

The battery eliminator circuit of Figure 15 is given as a practical example of a circuit employing a simple series regulator. The unit is designed for use with transistor radios, or other 9 volt battery equipment having a maximum current consumption of up to about 100 mA. It is not suitable for use with items of equipment which require a fairly high level of current, such as cassette recorders.

The circuit can be built as an external power supply which plugs into the power socket on the radio (it is an easy matter to add a suitable polarised socket if one is not already fitted), or it can be made small enough to fit into the battery compartment of the radio.

T1 is a 12 − 0 − 12 volt 100 mA transformer which provides safety isolation and a voltage step-down, and its centre tapped secondary winding feeds a straight forward push-pull full wave rectifier and smoothing capacitor. This gives an unloaded d.c. output of about 18 volts, dropping to about 12 volts at full load.

32

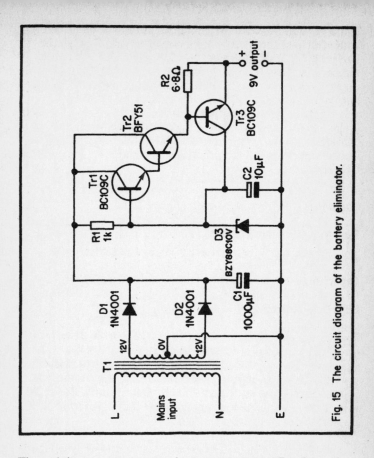

Fig. 15 The circuit diagram of the battery eliminator.

The stabiliser circuit is a simple series type using R1, D3 and C2 to provide a stabilised potential having a nominal level of 10 volts. The zener current varies from about 8 mA under zero load conditions down to about 3 mA at full load. The dissipation in both R1 and D3 is therefore very low, and low power devices can be used in both positions.

A Darlington pair emitter follower is used as the output buffer amplifier, and the combined current gain of Tr1 and Tr2 is typically about 30,000 at maximum output, and has a minimum

33

figure of about 10,000. With an input current of about 3 mA under full load conditions, and a minimum gain through the buffer amplifier of approximately 10,000, there is very little variation in the voltage drop through the amplifier with varying load currents. The actual voltage drop through the output amplifier is about 1.3 volts, and with a nominal 10 volt input this gives an output of approximately 8.7 volts. This is close enough to the required figure of 9 volts when one considers that the actual output voltage of a 9 volt battery varies from about 9.5 volts down to only about 7.5 volts during its lifespan.

Components Battery Eliminator (Figure 15)

Resistors. (Both are 1/3 watt 5%).
R1   1k
R2   6.8 ohms

Capacitors
C1   1000 μF 25V
C2   10 μF 25V

Semiconductors
Tr1   BC109C
Tr2   BFY51
Tr3   BC109C
D1   1N4001
D2   1N4001
D3   BZY88C10V (10V, 400 mW zener diode)

Transformer
T1   Standard mains primary, 12 – 0 – 12 volt 100 mA
          secondary

Miscellaneous
Case, output connector, mains lead, circuit board, wire, solder etc.

Current Limiting

In this type of circuit it is normal to incorporate some form of output short circuit protection. The reason this is necessary is that in order to give good regulation the unit must have a very low output impedance. Because of this very low source impedance a very high output current will flow if the output of the unit is accidentally short circuited. This could easily result in the output transistor, and possibly some of the other components, being almost instantly destroyed. An ordinary fuse is not likely to provide adequate protection as the damage would almost certainly be done before the fuse blew and cut off the supply.

The most common form of short circuit protection, and the one used here, is current limiting. This consists of additional circuitry which has no significant effect under normal operating conditions, but which causes the output voltage to rapidly decline if too low an impedance is placed across the output. In fact the output voltage reduces so rapidly with increased loading, that even with a short circuit placed across the output the current supplied by the unit is little more than its designed maximum level. The effect of a current limiting circuit is shown in the graph of Figure 16 which shows output voltage

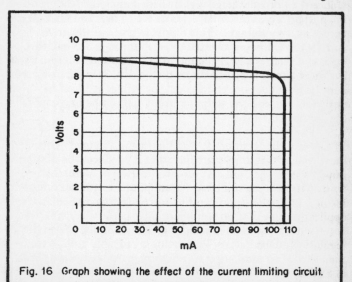

Fig. 16 Graph showing the effect of the current limiting circuit.

and current for a steadily decreasing load impedance, as obtained from the prototype Battery Eliminator unit.

The current limiting circuitry uses just two components; R2 and Tr3. It is so rapid in operation that there is no real risk of a short circuit on the output causing any damage to the output transistor or other components. The current limiting functions in the following manner.

R2 is connected in series with the output, and the voltage developed across this component is therefore proportional to the output current. At currents of up to about 100 mA the voltage developed across R2 will not be sufficient to switch on Tr3, which is a silicon type and has a stand-off voltage of about 0.65 volts.

At output currents of more than about 100 mA, the voltage across R2 gives Tr3 a strong enough forward bias to bring it into conduction. It then diverts some of the input current for Tr1 to the negative supply rail via the load. This tends to reduce the output voltage slightly. Increasing the loading on the output causes the voltage across R2 to rise, and takes Tr3 harder into conduction. This results in more of the drive current for Tr1 being diverted to earth through Tr3 and the load, and there is a large reduction in the output voltage. Even if a short circuit is placed across the output, Tr3 will be biased hard into conduction, and the output voltage reduced to virtually zero, and the output current will not be much more than about 100 mA.

In this way the required current limiting is obtained. One drawback of this simple circuit is that R2 reduces the output impedance of the unit, and produces a drop of about 0.65 volts in the output voltage between minimum and maximum loading, as can be seen from Figure 16. In this particular application this is of no real importance because a 9 volt battery has an internal resistance of several ohms, and so the regulation of the Battery Eliminator is probably still better than that of an ordinary 9 volt battery, even a large type such as a PP9.

In applications where the loss of regulation efficiency produced by the current limiting circuitry would be unacceptable, the current limit sense resistor must be added at the input of the regulator circuitry, and not at the output. One method of achieving this is shown in Figure 17.

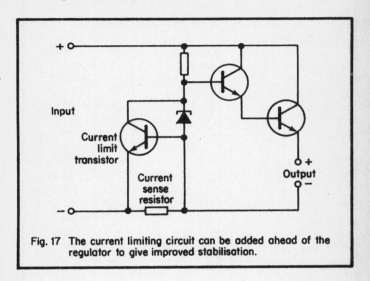

Fig. 17 The current limiting circuit can be added ahead of the regulator to give improved stabilisation.

High Performance Regulators

Another method of overcoming this problem is to use a more complicated, but very high performance regulator, where the circuit compares the output voltage to a highly stable reference voltage, and maintains the two at precisely the same level by means of a feedback action. This type of circuit automatically compensates for changes in the output voltage due to losses in the current limiting circuitry, and, in fact, compensates for all changes in the output voltage, whatever the cause.

Figure 18 shows in block diagram form the basic arrangement of this type of regulator. The non-inverting (+) input of an operational amplifier is fed from a highly stable reference

37

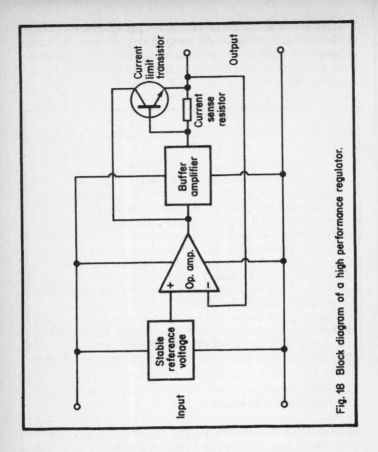

Fig. 18 Block diagram of a high performance regulator.

voltage source. This could be a simple zener stabiliser, a zener diode fed from a constant current source so as to give improved results, or some other form of improved reference source.

The output of the operational amplifier is taken to the output of the supply via a buffer amplifier which gives a high output current capability, and a current limiting circuit of the type described earlier. Negative feedback is applied from the output of the supply to the inverting (−) input of the operational amplifier.

38

An operational amplifier has an extremely high voltage gain, the gain of most devices being typically about 100,000 or 200,000 times! What the device is actually amplifying is the voltage difference across the two inputs. If the inverting input is the one which is at the higher potential, the output goes negative. If it is the non-inverting input that is at the higher voltage, the output goes positive.

Due to the negative feedback from the output to the inverting input, the output is stabilised at the reference voltage. As the reference voltage is highly stable, so is the output voltage as well.

The stabilisation process functions in the following manner. If the output should be at a higher potential than the reference source, the inverting input of the operational amplifier will obviously be at a higher voltage than the non-inverting input. This causes the output to go negative to a point where the two input voltages are balanced, remembering that the operational amplifier has a very high level of voltage gain, and a minute voltage across the inputs is enough to produce a considerable change in the output voltage. If the output voltage should drop below the reference voltage, this again produces a voltage difference across the inputs, this time of the opposite polarity, causing the output to swing positive. It can only swing sufficiently positive to balance the inputs, because as we have already seen, if it should go excessively positive, the inputs will be unbalanced and the output will be sent negative to correct the error. In this type of circuit the operational amplifier is sometimes referred to as an 'error amplifier', since it does infact amplify any error in the output voltage. But more than this, its output is used to correct the error.

In simple discrete circuits of this type the operational amplifier is often a very simple circuit which has only a fairly low voltage gain. While this does not give a level of performance equal to that which can be obtained using a proper high gain amplifier, in practice it still gives perfectly adequate results with the output normally being stabilised to within 100 mV or so of its nominal level, and sometimes considerably better than this.

Note that because the feedback to the inverting input is taken from output of the supply and not from the output of the buffer amplifier, the stabilisation action compensates for variations in output voltage due to changes in the voltage dropped across the current sense resistor.

Three-Terminal Regulators

It is becoming increasingly uncommon to find discrete voltage regulators of the type described above in new designs. High performance monolithic voltage regulators are available at quite low prices these days, and it is usually much less expensive and easier to use one of these, than to produce a discrete equivalent.

These i.c.s are extremely simple to use, as can be seen from the circuit diagram of Figure 19 which shows the basic way in which these devices are employed. The three terminals are, for obvious reasons, called the input, common and output. The input voltage is simply taken to the input and common terminals, and the stabilised voltage is available across the output and common terminals. The only discrete components required are a capacitor across the input and another across the output. These are both needed to aid the stability of the regulator, and the one at the output also helps to give the supply a good transient response. The values of these capacitors are not critical, and are usually 100 nf, 220 nf or 330 nf.

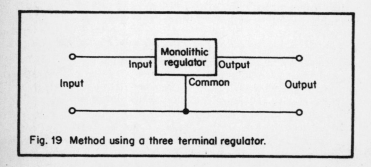

Fig. 19 Method using a three terminal regulator.

Types Available

The most popular types of fixed voltage monolithic voltage regulators are the 78 . . series positive regulators, and the 79 . . series negative regulators. These are available in three output current ratings. This gives nine positive types and nine negative types, as shown in the table provided below.

Positive Types

Voltage	100 mA max.	500 mA max.	1A max.
5	78L05	78M05	7805
12	78L12	78M12	7812
15	78L15	78M15	7815

Negative Types

	100 mA max.	500 mA max.	1A max.
5	79L05	79M05	7905
12	79L12	79M12	7912
15	79L15	79M15	7915

Most supplies have additional voltages in both positive and negative types, typical voltages for these being 8, 9, 10, 18 and 24 volts. Some devices have suffix letters or numbers, depending on the particular manufacturer concerned, but they are all basically the same. Many component retailers do not actually sell these regulators by type number, but simply state the polarity, voltage and current ratings, and possibly the type of encapsulation the device has. There is actually a very wide range of these devices available, and it is possible to find a suitable type for most applications.

These devices have current limiting output short circuit protection, and in medium and high power types this is normally of the foldback type. Foldback current limiting is where an overload on the output is not merely counteracted by the output current being limited to a safe level, but by the output current actually reducing! The response of a foldback current limiting circuit is shown in Figure 20, which clearly shows how the output current reduces under overload conditions to typically less than half the maximum output current.

The main reason for using foldback current limiting is that it substantially reduces the dissipation in the regulator under short circuit conditions. For example, if a regulator has an input voltage of 10 volts under full load, and provides an output current of up to 1 amp. and an output of 5 volts, under full load there is 5 volts dropped across the regulator and it passes 1 amp. This obviously gives a maximum dissipation of 5 watts.

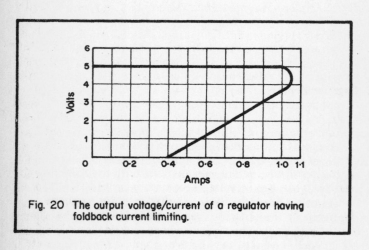

Fig. 20 The output voltage/current of a regulator having foldback current limiting.

Under short circuit conditions there will still be an output current of 1 amp. or thereabouts if straightforward current limiting is used, and the input voltage will still be 10 volts. However, this full 10 volts would be developed across the regulator, giving a dissipation of 10 watts, exactly double the normal working maximum dissipation in the device.

With foldback current limiting the full 10 volt supply would still be developed across the regulator, but the short circuit current might be, say 400 mA, giving a dissipation in the device of only 4 watts. This is less than the maximum power developed in the regulator under normal working conditions, and there is no danger of the device burning out.

Most monolithic voltage regulators also have thermal shutdown protection circuitry which reduces the output current if the device should start to overheat. These i.c.s. are therefore very hardy, and not easily destroyed by misuse.

One way they can be damaged is by an excessive input voltage. There are differences in the maximum permissible input voltages quoted by various manufacturers for devices of the same basic type, but 25 volts seems to be the lowest quoted for any 5 volt device. Higher voltage devices are capable of withstanding at least 30 volts, and for 20 and 24 volt types the figure is 40 volts.

For the circuit to function properly the input voltage must not drop below 2.5 volts more than the output voltage, except for 5 volt types where it must not be less than 2 volts above the output potential.

The quiescent current of these i.c.s. is between about 1 and 5 mA, apart from a few very high power types which have a quiescent current of 10 mA. The line regulation for most types is less than 1% (i.e. varying the input voltage from the minimum to the maximum acceptable level causes a change in the output voltage of less than 1%). The load regulation is also typically less than 1% for most of these i.c.s. (i.e. varying the output current from zero to maximum causes a change in the output potential of less than 1%). The majority of devices have a ripple rejection figure of about 60 dB, and an output noise level of less than 100 microvolts.

When using these devices it is important to keep in mind that they can only handle a limited power dissipation, and the input voltage under full load should not be more than a few volts higher than the output voltage. The maximum power rating in free air of the low, medium, and high power types is 0.7 watts, 1 watt and and 2 watts respectively. These are raised to 1.7 watts, 5 watts and 15 watts respectively with the device mounted on an infinite heat sink (which cannot, of course, be quite achieved in practice). The power dissipated in the device is equal to the difference between the input and output voltages, multiplied by the output current.

15V 800 mA Supply

As an example of a power supply design using a fixed voltage monolithic voltage regulator, we will assume that we require a supply to deliver (say) +15 volts at up to 800 mA. This can be provided using the circuit shown in Figure 21.

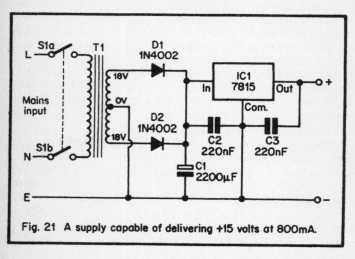

Fig. 21 A supply capable of delivering +15 volts at 800mA.

At the input there is on/off switch S1 and step-down transformer T1. The latter is an $18 - 0 - 18$ volt type with a secondary current rating of 1 amp. It feeds a push-pull full wave rectifier and an unloaded voltage of about 27 volts is produced across smoothing capacitor C1. A higher voltage transformer, such as a $20 - 0 - 20$ volt type, is not really suitable as the unloaded d.c. voltage produced would be about 30 volts, and could easily be a little more. This is equal to or above the maximum input voltage that most 7815 i.c.s can take, and is therefore unacceptable. Some types do actually have a maximum input voltage rating of 35 volts, and could be used

44

with a 20 volt transformer perfectly safely, provided that the constructor is sure that the device he or she is using is a 35 volt type. However, this would give increased power dissipation in the regulator.

A 15 volt type would not be suitable unless it had a fairly high current rating of about 2 amps or so, as the loaded supply voltage at the input of the regulator would otherwise be less than the minimum of 17.5 volts required by the regulator for proper operation.

C2 and C3 are the input and output decoupling capacitors for regulator device IC1, and these two capacitors should be mounted physically close to the regulator i.c. The 7815 is the obvious choice for IC1 since it is the smallest 15 volt positive regulator capable of handling the required maximum current of 800 mA.

Under full load there will be an input voltage to IC1 of something in the region of 19 to 20 volts, giving as much as 5 volts across the regulator. With a current of 800 mA this gives a dissipation of as much as 4 watts (0.8A x 5V = 4W). This is double the maximum of 2 watts that the 7815 can handle, and so the additional 2 watts must be 'dumped' into a heatsink.

A wide range of commercially made heatsinks are produced, and these are given a rating of so many degrees per watt. This is simply the rise in temperature that occurs for each watt of energy transferred into the heatsink, and the larger the heatsink, the lower the number of degrees per watt. The minimum amount of heatsinking required is calculated in the following way.

We must first know the maximum air temperature in which the equipment is to be used, and unless the equipment is going to be used in an unusually hot environment 30 degrees Centigrade is a safe assumption. It is then necessary to know the maximum safe temperature for the i.c., and for monolithic regulators this is 125 degrees Centigrade. However, this is the junction temperature, and not the case temperature that can be tolerated. The maximum acceptable case temperature is about

45

100 degrees Centigrade. This means that the device must not be allowed to rise by more than 70 degrees Centigrade (from 30 degrees to 100 degrees = 70 degrees).

As a power of 2 watts must cause an increase in temperature of no more than 70 degrees, a heatsink having a rating of 35 degrees Centigrade per watt or less (70 degrees divided by 2 watts = 35 degrees C. per watt) is required. In practice a somewhat larger heatsink is needed, as even using silicon grease or a substitute between the i.c. and the heatsink, there will be less than a 100% transfer of heat from one to the other. Also, in the interests of good long term reliability is is not advisable to have the i.c. operating just below its maximum safe temperature. If possible it should work below this level with a safety margin of 20 degrees or more. A small bolt-on heatsink having a rating of about 17 degrees Centigrade per watt is therefore the smallest heatsink that is likely to be satisfactory in practice, and a larger type should be used if possible.

If the regulator i.c. is mounted inside an enclosed case where it will not be in free air, but a pocket of trapped air that will be heated by the regulator and probably by other components inside the case as well, an even larger heatsink would be needed. How much larger depends upon the individual circumstances, but it would typically need to be two or even three times as large.

If the equipment is to be housed in a metal case, or a case having a metal chassis, the case or chassis can usually be used to provide adequate heatsinking. It is not normally necessary to insulate the regulator from the heatsink, case, or chassis, as the heat-tab of the regulator connects to the common terminal internally, and so the heatsink, case, chassis, and heat-tab will normally all be at the same potential.

Note that if a negative output version of the supply is required, it is merely necessary to reverse the polarity of D1, D2 and C1, and to replace IC1 with a 7915 device.

Capacitors
C1   2200 μF 40V
C2   220 nF plastic foil
C3   220 nF plastic foil

Semiconductors
IC1   7815 (15 volt, 1 amp. positive regulator)
D1   1N4002
D2   1N4002

Transformer
T1   Standard mains primary, 18 − 0 − 18V,
            1 amp secondary.

Switch
S1   D.P.S.T. rotary mains or toggle switch

Miscellaneous
Case, output sockets, circuit board, mains lead, wire, solder
etc.

Dual Supply

Because fixed voltage monolithic regulators are available in
both negative and positive versions, they are ideal for use where
dual balanced supplies are required. If, for example, a supply
is required for an operational amplifier-based circuit requiring
positive and negative supplies of 12 volts at 100 mA, the circuit
of Figure 22 could be used.

Here T1 is a 15 − 0 − 15 volt transformer having a secondary
current rating of 200 mA or more. There are two push-pull
full wave rectifiers; D2 and D3 which provide a positive output,
and D1 plus D4 which provide a negative output. The positive
supply is smoothed by C1 and the negative one is smoothed by
C2. IC1 provides regulation of the positive supply, and IC2
acts as the negative supply regulator. C3 to C6 are the
decoupling capacitors for the regulators, and should be mounted
physically close to their respective devices in order to ensure
good stability.

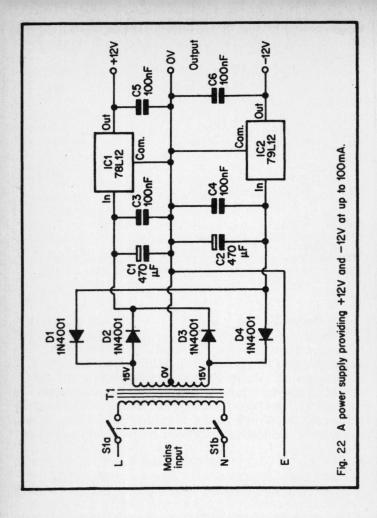

Fig. 22 A power supply providing +12V and −12V at up to 100mA.

The power developed across each regulator will be several hundred milliwatts, and both devices will operate quite hot if the maximum 100 mA (or virtually the full 100 mA) is drawn from the unit continuously. However, it is unlikely that any heatsinking will be needed.

48

Capacitors
C1, C2   470 μF 25V (2 off)
C3 to C6   100 nF plastic foil (4 off)

Semiconductors
IC1   78L12 (12 volt, 100 mA. positive regulator)
IC2   79L12 (12 volt, 100 mA. negative regulator)
D1 to D4   1N4001 (4 off)

Transformer
T1   Standard mains primary, 15 − 0 −15 volt 200 mA
           (or more) secondary

Switch
S1   D.P.S.T. rotary mains or toggle switch

Miscellaneous
Case, output sockets, circuit board, mains lead, wire, solder
etc.

Higher Output Voltage

The method shown in Figure 22 can also be used when the
required output voltage is higher than can be obtained using a
single regulator. For example, two 15 volt regulators used in
this arrangement will provide 30 volts, and two 24 volt types
give 48 volts. The 0V output is ignored, and the output is
taken from across the positive and negative outputs only. The
appropriate connection should be connected to the mains earth
lead.

Increased Output Voltage

Although there is an increasingly large range of voltages
available these days, there is by no means a regulator to suit
every requirement. It is possible to obtain a small increase in
the output voltage from a voltage regulator by using a few
additional components, and this method helps to fill in some
of the voltages for which no regulator is available. This basic

method of obtaining this increased output voltage is shown in Figure 23.

Here it has been assumed that the desired output voltage is approximately 6V. This can be obtained using a 5 volt regulator in a circuit designed to boost the output by 1 volt, and this is achieved by merely adding two silicon rectifiers in the common lead of the regulator, as shown in the diagram. The rectifiers are connected so that they are forward biased by the quiescent current which is drawn by the regulator, and which flows through the common terminal. The rectifiers therefore act rather like low voltage zener diodes, each having a zener voltage of about 0.5 to 0.6 volts, and giving a combined zener voltage of about 1 to 1.2 volts.

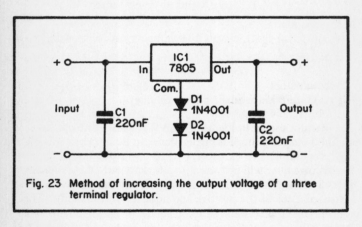

Fig. 23   Method of increasing the output voltage of a three terminal regulator.

Their effect is to raise the common terminal of the regulator to 1 volt or so above the earth rail potential. The regulator actually stabilises the output at 5 volts above the common terminal's potential, and not 5 volts above the earth rail. Therefore, by raising the common terminal by 1 volt or so, the output is raised by the same amount, bringing it to the required level of 6 volts or marginally more.

This method can be used with any three terminal regulator, although with some small types the author has come across, it has been necessary to add a resistor of a few kilohms in value between the output and common terminals in order to obtain satisfactory operation. The amount by which the output is raised can be altered by varying the number of rectifiers used. Ordinary small silicon diodes such as the 1N4148 can also be used, but the output is then raised by about 0.6 to 0.7 volts per diode. It is also possible to use a zener diode or amplified diode to raise the potential at the common terminal, but it is not advisable to attempt to obtain a rise in the output potential of more than a few volts. This arrangement also works with the 79 . . series of negative voltage regulators, provided the diode(s) or transistor is connected with the correct polarity.

The current limiting and thermal protection circuits of the regulators still function satisfactorily when the method described here is used.

Components (Figure 23)

Semiconductors
IC1   7805 (5 volt, 1 amp regulator)
D1, D2   1N4001 (2 off)

Capacitors
C1, C2   220 nF plastic foil (2 off)

Increased Current

It is possible to obtain increased output current from a monolithic voltage regulator, and one method of doing so is shown in the circuit diagram of Figure 24. The ratio of R1 to R2 ensures that for each milliamp of current that flows in R1, D1 and the regulator, a little over 4 mA is directed through Tr1 and R2. Thus with the full 1 amp passing through IC1, there is a current of over 4 amps flowing through Tr1, and the circuit provides a maximum output current of slightly in excess of 5 amps.

Even in the event of an overload, the currents through Tr1 and

51

IC1 still have a ratio of slightly more than 4 to 1, and so the current limiting is still effective.

Circuits of this type are becoming unnecessary these days due to the arrival of very high power regulators such as the 78H05, 78H12 etc., which have a maximum current rating of 5 amps, and are used in precisely the same way as the other three terminal monolithic regulators.

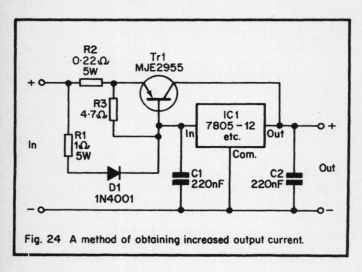

Fig. 24 A method of obtaining increased output current.

Components (Figure 24)

Resistors
R1   1 ohm 5 watt 5%
R2   0.22 ohms 5 watt 5%
R3   4.7 ohms ½ watt 10%

Capacitors
C1, C2   220 nF plastic foil (2 off)

Semiconductors
Tr1   MJE2955
D1   1N4001
IC1   1 amp positive regulator

CHAPTER 3

VARIABLE VOLTAGE SUPPLIES

Variable voltage stabilised supplies are basically the same as
fixed voltage types, but have a potentiometer added into the
circuit at the appropriate point. Circuits of this type are
primarily used as bench and workshop power supplies, but
they can also be used where an item of equipment requires a
supply voltage that would be difficult to produce using a fixed
voltage circuit. In this case the potentiometer is a preset type
which is used to trim the output voltage of the supply to the
desired level.

Simple Bench Supply

The circuit of Figure 25 is for a simple bench power supply
that will provide an output voltage which is continuously
variable from zero to slightly more than 12 volts. A maximum
current of over 500 mA is available, and the noise and ripple
on the output are no more than about 1 mV at any output
current and voltage within the working range of the unit. The
maximum variation in the output voltage between minimum
and maximum loading is only about 300 mV. The unit is
suitable for testing and developing most electronic projects,
although it does not have sufficient output for high power
equipment, such as audio power amplifiers having an output
of more than a few watts.

T1 is a transformer having a secondary rated at 18 volts and
1 amp, or a 9 − 0 − 9 volt type can be used if the centre tap is
ignored. A 17 volt 1 amp battery charger transformer is also
suitable. Its output is full wave rectified by the bridge rectifier
formed by D1 to D4, and the output from the rectifier is well
smoothed by C1.

The regulator is basically the same as that shown in Figure 13(b),
and described in the previous chapter. The only difference is

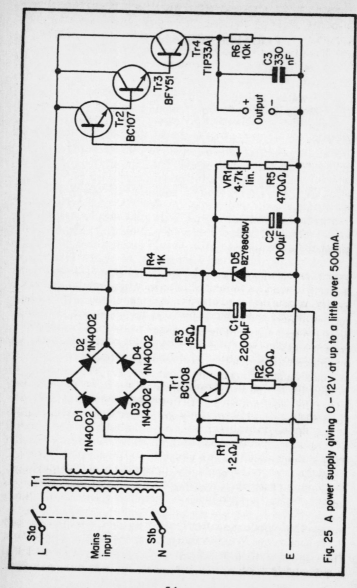

Fig. 25 A power supply giving 0 – 12V at up to a little over 500mA.

54

that a potential divider circuit has been added between the output of the zener stabiliser, and the input to the buffer amplifier. This potential divider is formed by VR1 and R5, and the output at VR1's slider can be varied from only about 1.4 volts when it is at the bottom of its track, up to the nominal 15 volt zener voltage when it is at the top of its track. There is approximately 2 volts dropped through the output buffer stage, giving an output voltage range from zero up to typically 13 volts. However, the upper limit is subject to component tolerances, such as the 5% tolerance on the zener voltage, and so the maximum output potential is only guaranteed to be a little in excess of 12 volts.

Some form of effective overload protection circuit is really essential in a bench power supply, where frequent accidental overloads and short circuits are likely to occur. In this circuit simple current limiting is used, and is provided by Tr1 and its associated components.

Under normal operating conditions the voltage developed across R1, which is connected in series with the output of the supply, is insufficient to bias Tr1 into conduction. The circuit is then allowed to function normally, apart from a small and insignificant voltage drop across R1. This does not adversely effect the regulation efficiency of the unit since it has been added ahead of the regulator circuitry.

If an overload occurs, the voltage across R1 will rise to about 0.65 volts, and Tr1 will be switched on by the base current it receives via current limiting resistor R2. A fairly strong current is then drawn through Tr1 and current limiting resistor R3, causing an increased voltage drop across R4, and the output voltage to be reduced. This limits the output current to no more than about 550 to 600 mA even with a short circuit on the output, as the current limit circuitry then reduces the output voltage to virtually zero.

R6 is a load resistor and merely ensures that the output current never becomes so low that the buffer amplifier fails to operate properly, producing the wrong output voltage. C3 helps to give the unit a good transient response.

The power dissipated in Tr4 depends upon the output voltage and current, and is at a maximum with low output voltages and high output currents (or the output short circuited, which gives the same effect). Under worst case conditions there is likely to be about 20 volts across Tr4, and it will be passing a current of about 600 mA. This gives a power dissipation in the device of around 12 watts. In order to withstand this indefinitely it should be mounted on a substantial heatsink. A type having a rating of about 3 degrees Centigrade per watt should be satisfactory even if the device is mounted inside an unventilated case. A smaller type having a rating of about 4.5 degrees Centigrade per watt should be suitable if the device is mounted in free air.

VR1 can be fitted with a large control knob having a scale calibrated in terms of output voltage. A multimeter can be used when calibrating this. Alternatively a voltmeter can be added across the output, but the problem here is that it is unlikely that a meter having an ideal full scale value will be obtainable. Voltmeters having fairly high full scale values are readily available, but would not give an acceptable level of accuracy at the relatively low voltages involved here. It may be possible to obtain a 0 to 15 volt type, and this would be perfectly suitable. The alternative is to use a current meter with a suitable series resistor to give the required full scale value.

The value of the required resistor is given by dividing the required full scale voltage by the full scale current reading of the meter. Thus in order to obtain a full scale value of (say) 15 volts with a 100 μA f.s.d. meter, the resistor must have a value of 15 volts divided by 0.0001 amps (100 μA) which equals 150,000 ohms, or 150k in other words. Actually this gives the required total resistance for the meter and the series resistor, and so the coil resistance of the meter should be subtracted from the answer. However, in practice, when a f.s.d. value of several volts or more is required, the resistance of the meter will be so low in comparison with the series resistor that it can be ignored. If the calculated resistance does not coincide with a preferred value, the nearest preferred value can be selected provided it is within about 1% of the calculated value. If not, then two or more resistors connected in series must be used to make up the required value. The series resistor or resistors should have a close tolerance of 2% or better. The meter should obviously not have a very high f.s.d. value, or it would heavily load the power supply. A f.s.d. value of about 1 mA or less is suitable.

An alternative method is to use a preset resistor in series with the meter, and this can be used to set the voltmeter sensitivity at the correct level using a multimeter as a calibration standard. The value of the preset can be calculated using the method described above, and then adding 50 to 100% to the answer. A preferred value in which presets are available should fall within this range, or close to one of the limits.

One problem with using a current meter plus series resistor as a voltmeter is that it will almost certainly be necessary to recalibrate the meter. Most modern meters have a plastic front section which simply clips on and off. With this removed, the unwanted scale markings can usually be carefully scratched off with the point of a compass, or if this tends to remove both the markings and the white overall covering of the scale plate, it might be better to paint out the markings using white enamel paint. Various forms of rub-on and stick-on lettering and numbering are available, and it is not too difficult to recalibrate a meter scale using these.

If recalibration of a meter is undertaken, it should be borne in mind that a meter movement is very delicate, and is easily damaged. Great care must therefore be taken to avoid damaging the meter movement once the front cover of the meter has been removed. The scale plate of every meter the author has come across is easily removed from the rest of the meter, and it is normally just a matter of removing two small screws. Recalibration will probably be much easier if this is done, and the risk of the meter becoming damaged will almost certainly be considerably reduced.

Components 0 – 12 Volt, 500 mA. Supply (Figure 25)

Resistors. (All 1/3 watt 5%).

R1	1.2 ohms
R2	100 ohms
R3	15 ohms
R4	1k
R5	470 ohms
R6	10k
VR1	4.7k lin. carbon

Capacitors

C1	2200 μF 40V
C2	100 μF 25V
C3	330 nF plastic foil

Semiconductors

Tr1	BC108
Tr2	BC107
Tr3	BFY51
Tr4	TIP33A
D1 to D4	1N4002 (4 off)
D5	BZY88C15V (15 volt, 400 mW zener)

Transformer

T1	Standard mains primary, 17 or 18 volt, 1 amp secondary

Switch

S1	D.P.S.T. rotary mains or toggle type

Miscellaneous

Case, output sockets, circuit board, mains lead, wire, solder etc.

Current Meter

An output current meter is a very useful feature to have on a workshop power supply, and it can quickly show up an excessive current consumption by the supplied equipment, enabling remedial action to be taken before serious damage occurs to the supplied equipment.

While it is possible to simply add a current meter of a suitable full scale value in series with the output, this does have the disadvantage of reducing the output impedance of the supply, and degrading the regulation efficiency. It would be preferable to add the meter ahead of the regulator circuit. For example, an output current meter could be added to the circuit of Figure 25 between the junction of D2, D4, C1 and R4, and the junction of Tr2 to Tr4 collectors. The meter would then read fractionally high as it would register the small quiescent output current as well as the current drawn by the load. This is of no real practical consequence though, as the quiescent current drawn by the output buffer amplifier is so low in comparison to the full scale value of the meter (which could be 500 mA or 1 A in this example).

An alternative method of adding an output current meter to the unit is shown in Figure 26. Here the current sense resistor of the current limiting circuit (R1) is used as the shunt resistor for a sensitive current meter, and reduces its sensitivity to the correct level. The resistance through the meter circuit is very high when compared to the resistance of R1, and so the addition of the meter circuit does not have any significant effect on the current limiting circuitry.

R1 is connected in series with the output, and the voltage developed across this resistance is therefore proportional to the output current (if we ignore the small and insignificant

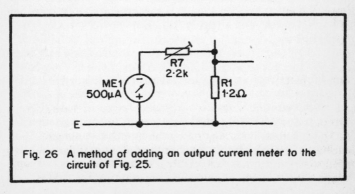

Fig. 26   A method of adding an output current meter to the circuit of Fig. 25.

current drawn by the regulator circuitry). ME1 and R7 effectively form a voltmeter circuit which registers the voltage developed across R1, and R7 is adjusted to give a full scale sensitivity of 0.6V. From Ohms Law it is apparent that in order to give 0.6V across R1, an output current of 500 mA (0.5A) is required (I = E/R, I = 0.6 ÷ 1.2, = 0.5A). The meter thus effectively reads 0 to 500 mA., and does not need any recalibration as it already has a 0 to 500 scale.

There is no need to include any meter overload protection circuitry when including an output current meter in a power supply which has current limiting overload protection, since the current limiting prevents any serious overloading of the meter from occuring.

Components Optional Meter Circuit (Figure 26)

R7   2.2k 0.25W preset
ME1   500 μA. moving coil panel meter

The 723C I.C.

The 723C integrated circuit is a 'standard' i.c. voltage regulator which has been designed to be capable of fulfilling most voltage regulator applications. It can be used as a positive regulator, negative regulator, and as a switching regulator (a highly efficient type of circuit where the output buffer stage is switched on and off at high speed, and dissipates very little power). It can be connected to give straightforward current limiting or foldback current limiting. There is far too little space available here to describe this device in detail, together with the various ways of utilizing it, but the more important aspects of the device will be considered.

The output voltage range of the device is 2 volts minimum up to 37 volts maximum. The maximum permissible output current is 150 mA., but in practice the output current will often need to be limited to considerably less than this figure to keep within the maximum permissible dissipation for the device, which is 500 mW. The maximum input voltage should be no more than 50 volts peak, and 40 volts continuous. The minimum input voltage is 9.5 volts, or 3 volts more than the maximum output voltage required, whichever is the greater. The maximum permissible input output voltage differential is 37 volts.

Figure 27 shows in block diagram form the basic arrangement of the 723C's internal circuitry. It consists of a highly stable reference voltage having a nominal potential of 7 volts, an operational amplifier, a buffer amplifier, and a current limiting transistor. It is really a regulator of the type previously outlined in the block diagram of Figure 18, and described in the previous chapter. However, instead of the inverting input of the operational amplifier being connected to the output of the circuit, it is brought out to a pin of the device. It is normally taken to the wiper contact of an external potentiometer connected across the output of the circuit. If the wiper of this potentiometer is taken to the top of its track, the circuit operates in exactly the same manner as the fixed voltage type outlined in Figure 18 and described in the previous chapter, with the output being stabilised at the same potential as the reference voltage.

If the slider of the potentiometer is brought down its track, rather than stabilising the output at the same potential as the reference voltage, the circuit stabilises the inverting input of the operational amplifier at this potential. Due to the voltage drop across the potentiometer, the output must rise to a higher potential in order to bring the inverting input to the appropriate voltage. The further down its track the slider is taken, the greater the voltage drop through the potentiometer, and the higher the output voltage becomes. If, for instance, the slider is taken two thirds of the way down its track, the voltage fed to the inverting input of the operational amplifier will only be one third of the output voltage. The output is thus stabilised at three times the reference voltage so that the appropriate voltage is maintained at the inverting input of the operational amplifier. Thus a variable output voltage is obtained, together with a very efficient stabilising action.

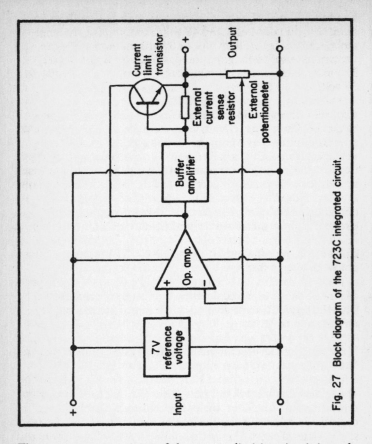

Fig. 27 Block diagram of the 723C integrated circuit.

The current sense resistor of the current limiting circuit is made of a discrete component so that the maximum output current can be varied to suit individual requirements.

The output voltage of the 723C is approximately equal to 7 (R1 + R2)/R2 volts, where R1 is the resistance between the output and the inverting input of the operational amplifier, and R2 is the resistance between the inverting input and the negative supply rail. This assumes that the reference voltage is coupled direct to the non-inverting input of the operational

62

amplifier, or these two points are coupled via a fairly low value resistor. It is not essential to do this, and the reference voltage can be fed to the non-inverting input via a potential divider, so that the reference voltage supplied to the operational amplifier is less than 7 volts. In fact it is essential to do this if an output voltage of less than 7 volts is required, since the output voltage cannot be less (under normal working conditions) than the reference voltage at the non-inverting input of the operational amplifier. The lowest reference voltage that can be successfully employed in a 723C based circuit is 2 volts. If a reference voltage of less than 7 volts is used, then the 7 in the above equation must be replaced by whatever reference voltage is used.

The value of the current limiting sense resistor is equal to 0.66 divided by the required maximum output current.

3.5 to 20V 1.5A Supply

Figure 28 shows a practical example of a circuit using the 723C integrated circuit, and this is for a bench power supply having an output voltage range of 3.5 to 20 volts nominal, and capable of providing a maximum output current of 1.5 amps. Three switched levels of current limiting are available at 15 mA., 150 mA., and 1.5A. (approximately).

The mains supply is taken to the primary winding of step down transformer T1 by way of on/off switch S1. LP1 is an on/off indicator lamp, and this is a neon type having an integral series resistor for 240V mains operation. The output from the secondary of T1, which has a rating of 20 volts at 2 amps or more, is full wave rectified by D1 to D4, and smoothed by C1.

In order to provide the minimum output voltage of 3.5 volts it is necessary to couple the output of the reference source at pin 6 of IC1 to the non-inverting input of the operational amplifier at pin 6 via a suitable potential divider. The potential divider is formed by R1 and R2, and as the two resistors have the same value, the 7 volt input is halved to give an output of 3.5 volts.

63

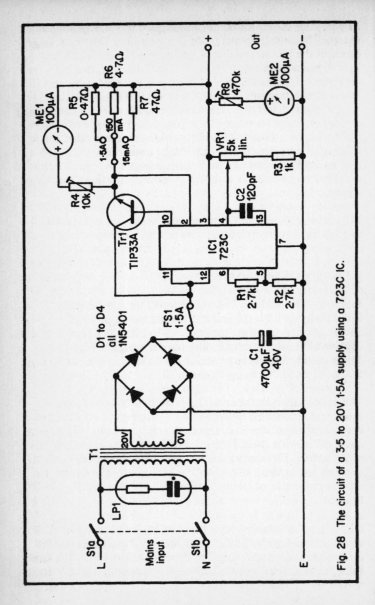

Fig. 28 The circuit of a 3·5 to 20V 1·5A supply using a 723C IC.

64

The positive output of the unregulated supply is connected to the positive supply terminal of IC1 (pin 12) and the positive input of the buffer amplifier in IC1 (pin 11) via fuse FS1. As the current and power handling capabilities of the 723C are inadequate for this application, the output terminal of the device (pin 10) is used to drive an emitter follower buffer stage using discrete transistor Tr1. This feeds the output from its emitter terminal via whichever of the three current limit sense resistors is selected using S2. These three resistors provide the three limit currents. ME1 is an output current meter, and this is of basically the same type as the one shown in Figure 26 and described earlier. R4 is adjusted to give a full scale value of 20 mA., 200 mA., and 2A. (the full scale value changes according to the current limit level selected). This is much better than having a straightforward 0 to 2A. current meter which would give no significant deflection at output currents of up to about 100 mA. or so, and would therefore be of comparatively little value. On the 15 mA. current limit range, where the meter reads 0 to 20 mA., there will be a small deflection of the meter under quiescent conditions due to the current drawn by VR1 and R3. This is unavoidable, but fortunately it is not really very troublesome in practice.

VR1 and R3 set the voltage range of the unit, and this is continuously variable from about 3.5 volts with VR1's slider at the top of its track, up to about 23 volts with the slider at the bottom of its track. The upper limit is purposely made rather more than the required limit of 20 volts so that even if the actual maximum output voltage is somewhat less than the theoretical value, due to component tolerances, the required figure of 20 volts should still be attainable. The lower limit of 3.5 volts is also a nominal one, and will vary somewhat from one unit to another. In order to minimise errors in the output voltage range it is advisable to make R1, R2 and R3 all 1 or 2% types.

C2 is the compensation capacitor for the operational amplifier contained within the 723C, and it aids good stability. R8 and ME2 form an output voltage meter circuit, and R8 is adjusted for a full scale sensitivity of 25 volts. With most 100 microamp meters this gives a convenient one scale division per volt.

Tr1 has to dissipate a power of around 30 watts at minimum output voltage and maximum output current, and it is therefore advisable to mount it on a large heatsink rated at about 2.5 degrees Centigrade per watt, and mounted on the exterior of the case. R5 has to dissipate about 1 watt under full output current conditions, and so it would be advisable to give this a conservative rating of 2 watts or more. In order to give good consistency between the three current meter ranges, R5 to R7 should have a tolerance of 5% or better.

Components 3.5 — 20 Volt, 1.5A Supply (Figure 28)

Resistors
R1	2.7k 1/3 watt 2% or better
R2	2.7k 1/3 watt 2% or better
R3	1k 1/3 watt 2% or better
R4	10k 0.25 watt preset
R5	0.47 ohms 2 watt 5%
R6	4.7 ohms 1/3 watt 5%
R7	47 ohms 1/3 watt 5%
R8	470k 0.25 watt preset
VR1	4.7k or 5k lin. carbon

Capacitors
C1	4700 μF 40V
C2	120 pF ceramic plate

Semiconductors
IC1	723C (14 pin DIL)
Tr1	TIP33A
D1 to D4	1N5401 (4 off)

Transformer
T1	Standard mains primary, 20 volt 2 amp secondary

Switches
S1	D.P.S.T. rotary mains or toggle type
S2	3 way single pole rotary type capable of switching 1.5A

Fuse
FS1	1.5A 20mm quick blow type

Lamp
LP1   Panel indicator neon having integral series resistor
           for use on 240V mains

Meters
ME1, ME2 100 μA. moving coil panel meters (2 off)

Miscellaneous
Case, output sockets, circuit board, mains lead, wire, 20mm
chassis mounting fuseholder, solder etc.

Four Terminal Regulators

A four terminal voltage regulator is very similar to the three
terminal type described in the previous chapter, but the
inverting input of the internal operational amplifier is taken out
to an additional terminal. This enables the output voltage to be
readily varied by means of a potentiometer connected across the
output, and feeding the additional (control) terminal of the
device.

The basic method of using a four terminal monolithic voltage
regulator is shown in Figure 29. This is very much the same as
for a three terminal type, with decoupling capacitors across the
output and input to aid good stability and transient response.
R1 and R2 form the potential divider which determines the

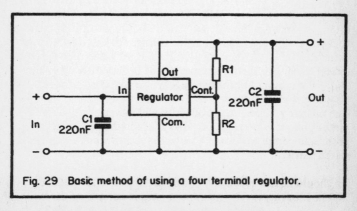

Fig. 29 Basic method of using a four terminal regulator.

output voltage. The output voltage is equal to (R1 + R2)/R1 multiplied by the internal reference voltage of the device. Of course, in practice R1 and R2 would normally be replaced by a potentiometer so as to give a variable output, or by several switched preset potentiometers if several switched output voltages are required. A simple potential divider can be used though, where the output voltage required is one that is not easily obtained using a fixed voltage monolithic voltage regulator. There is no point in using a four-terminal regulator in an application where a three-terminal type could be used, because the four-terminal variety are substantially more expensive.

Four Voltage Supply

Figure 30 shows an example of a power supply using a four terminal monolithic voltage regulator. This is for a power supply having four switched output voltages of 6V, 7.5V, 9V and 12V, with a maximum output current of 500 mA. This can be used when designing or testing battery operated equipment such as transistor radios and portable cassette recorders. It can also be used as a mains adaptor for equipment of this type which has a power socket (or if a power socket is added).

The circuit is very straightforward, and has the output from T1 full wave rectified by D1 and D2, and smoothed by C1. The regulator used is a μA78MGU1C type, which has a 5 volt internal reference voltage, and can therefore give voltages down to 5 volts. The maximum output voltage for this device is 30 volts, and the maximum input voltage is 40 volts. For correct operation the input voltage should not be less than two volts above the required output voltage.

The output voltage is controlled by whichever of the four preset potentiometers (R1 to R4) is selected by S2, and these presets are simply adjusted to give the four output voltages stated earlier.

T1 should have a secondary rating of 15 − 0 − 15 volts at 500 mA. or more. The maximum output current of the unit

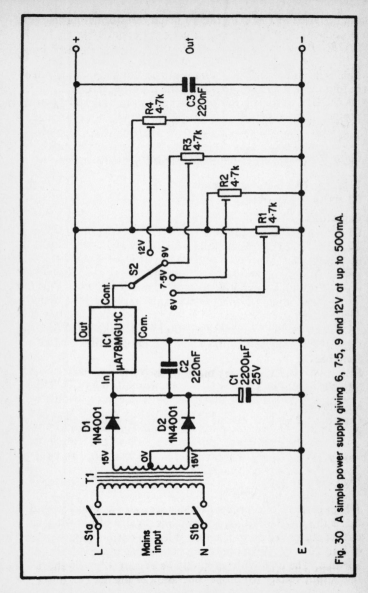

Fig. 30 A simple power supply giving 6, 7·5, 9 and 12V at up to 500mA.

can be raised to 1 amp by using a mains transformer having a
secondary current rating of 1 amp or more, and using a
µA78GU1C device in the IC1 position. IC1, regardless of
which type is used, should be mounted on a substantial heatsink as it has to dissipate several watts at certain combination of
output current and voltage. Both the µA78MGU1C and
µA78GU1C devices have foldback current limiting and thermal
protection circuitry.

Components Simple Power Supply (Figure 30)

Resistors. (All 0.25 watt presets).
R1 to R4   4.7k (4 off)

Capacitors
C1   2200 µF 25V
C2, C3   220 nF plastic foil (2 off)

Semiconductors
IC1   µA78MGU1C
D1, D2   1N4001 (2 off)

Transformer
T1   Standard mains primary, 15 − 0 − 15 volt 500 mA.
          secondary

Switches
S1   D.P.S.T. rotary mains or toggle type
S2   4 way 3 pole rotary (only one pole used)

Miscellaneous
Case, output sockets, circuit board, mains lead, wire, solder
etc.

High Current Type

A high current four-terminal voltage regulator is available, and
this is the µA78HGKC device which is capable of providing an
output current of up to 5 amps. It has an output voltage range
of 5 to 20 volts, and a maximum permissible input voltage of
25 volts. The input voltage should be at least 3.5 volts above
the output voltage for proper operation of the device. It is a

hybrid device which incorporates output current limiting and has thermal protection circuitry.

Figure 31 shows a simple circuit which employs this device, and this is for a bench power supply having an output voltage range of 5 to 15 volts (nominal) at a maximum current of 3 amps.

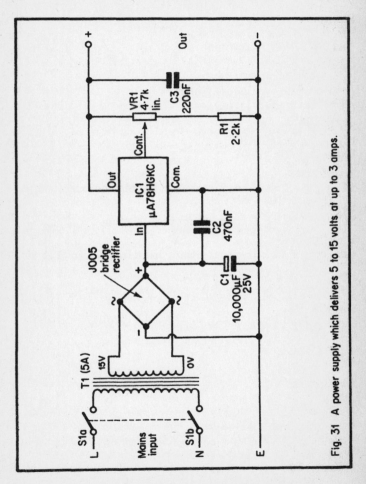

Fig. 31 A power supply which delivers 5 to 15 volts at up to 3 amps.

71

Negative versions of the four terminal voltage regulator devices mentioned here are available, and simply have a figure 9 in the type number instead of a figure 8 (µA79MGU1C etc.).

Components 5 – 15 Volts, 3 Amp Supply (Figure 31)

Resistors
R1   2.2k 1/3 watt 5%
VR1   4.7k lin. carbon

Capacitors
C1   10,000 µF 25V
C2   470 nF plastic foil
C3   220 nF plastic foil

Semiconductors
IC1   µA78HGKC
Bridge rectifier   J005

Transformer
T1   Standard mains primary, 15 volt 5 amp secondary

Switch
S1   D.P.S.T. rotary mains or toggle type

Miscellaneous
Case, output sockets, circuit board, mains lead, wire, solder etc.

CHAPTER 4

MISCELLANEOUS PROJECTS

This chapter will cover a number of designs for power supplies or power supply related projects, which do not fall into any of the categories covered in the previous chapters.

Car – Cassette Supply

If a cassette recorder is being powered from internal batteries, running costs are normally rather high due to the quite high current consumption of these devices (the motor for the deck usually requires several hundred milliamps). If the unit is being used at home, a great saving in running costs can be obtained by running it from the mains supply, either using an internal power supply if one is fitted, or by connecting an external supply to the power socket of the recorder if there is no built in supply. If the recorder is used in a car, it is again possible to obtain greatly reduced running costs, this time by powering the recorder from the car battery.

One problem here is that most car batteries have a nominal potential of 12 volts, whereas most cassette recorders are for 6, 7.5 or 9 volt operation. It is therefore necessary to interpose a voltage stabiliser having the appropriate output voltage, between the car battery and the recorder.

The circuit diagram of a simple regulator which is suitable for this application is shown in Figure 32. This is based on the μA78GU1C device which was covered in the previous chapter, and the operation of this device will not, therefore, be covered again here. The circuit will provide up to 1 amp (which should be sufficient for any cassette recorder) and the output voltage is continuously variable from approximately 5 volts to 10 volts, which includes the three normal cassette recorder supply voltages of 6, 7.5 and 9 volts.

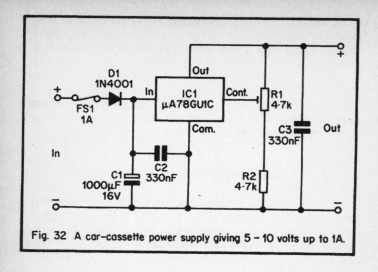

Fig. 32 A car-cassette power supply giving 5 – 10 volts up to 1A.

The input voltage is taken to the regulator i.c. via fuse FS1 and protective diode, D1. The latter blocks the input from the regulator device if the input is accidentally connected with the wrong polarity. The input voltage is likely to contain a substantial amount of noise, and C1 is used to combat this. Of course, the regulator also provides electronic smoothing of the output, and considerably reduces the noise level on the output; C2 and C3 are the normal decoupling capacitors for the regulator i.c. R1 and R2 form the potential divider which controls the output voltage. The nominal output potential is 5 volts with the slider of R1 at the upper end of its track, increasing to 10 volts (approximately) as it is moved down to the lower end of its track.

Of course, thermal overload protection circuitry and foldback current limiting are incorporated in the µA78GU1C, as mentioned in the previous chapter. The i.c. should be mounted on a reasonably substantial heatsink, and this could merely consist of the metal case for the project. The heat-tab of the µA78GU1C connects internally to its 'COM' terminal, and it is therefore unnecessary to insulate the heat-tab from the case (and the chassis of the car) in negative earth vehicles. However, it is

74

essential that IC1 is properly insulated from the case and the car's chassis if the vehicle is of the positive earth type, otherwise the supply will be short circuited! If the unit is used in a positive earth car, FS1 should be moved into the negative input lead, so that it protects the unit in the event of a short circuit caused by faulty insulation of IC1.

Components Car-Cassette Power Supply (Figure 32)

Resistors
R1	4.7k 0.25 watt preset
R2	4.7k 1/3 watt 5%

Capacitors
C1	1000 μF 16V
C2, C3	330 nF plastic foil (2 off)

Semiconductors
IC1	μA78GU1C
D1	1N4001

Fuse
FS1	20mm 1A. quick blow type

Miscellaneous
Case, circuit board, input and output leads, wire, 20mm chassis mounting fuseholder, solder etc.

Train Controller

Most simple train controllers consist of a step-down and isolation transformer driving a bridge rectifier and a large (in terms of wattage, not resistance) variable resistor. One problem with this simple arrangement is that it produces a high output impedance at low and medium speeds, and gives a tendency for the motor to stall. This occurs because an increase in the loading on the motor (caused by the train going up a gradient for example) results in it trying to draw more supply current. Due to the high output impedance of the supply, the increased loading by the motor causes a significant reduction in the output voltage of the supply, and the supply current only marginally increases. With the supply voltage actually reducing, the power fed to the motor could actually decrease! It then becomes quite likely that the motor will stall.

A better method is to use a stabilised supply having a continuously variable output of 0 to about 12 volts or so, and the circuit of a simple unit of this type is shown in Figure 33. T1 is the isolation and step-down transformer, and it has a

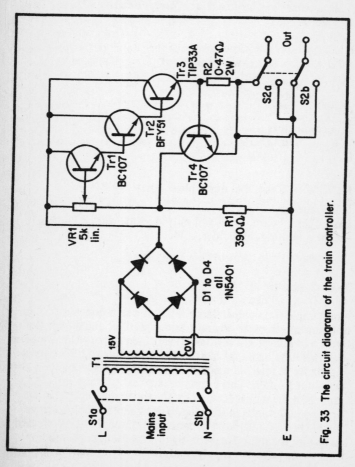

Fig. 33 The circuit diagram of the train controller.

secondary rating of 15 volts at 1.5 amps or more. Its output is full wave rectified by the bridge rectifier formed by D1 to D4, and then this rough d.c. output is fed to a simple voltage controller circuit. This does not provide a highly stable output, and is really just a potentiometer feeding a buffer amplifier. Thus the voltage set on VR1 is transferred to the low impedance output at Tr3's emitter, less the drop of about 2 volts incurred through the three transistors (Tr1 to Tr3) of the buffer amplifier. This simple arrangement gives adequate output stability for this application.

It is not necessary for the output of the supply to be smoothed, and it is in fact normal for d.c. motor supplies to have a pulsating d.c. output.

Tr4 and R2 provide output current limiting at a little over 1.4 amps (peak), and this protects the unit against damage if an accidental short circuit on the output should occur. S2 can be used to transpose the polarity of the output of the unit, and is the motor reversing switch.

Tr3 will dissipate several watts under certain operating conditions, and must be given a reasonable amount of heatsinking.

Components Train Controller (Figure 33)

Resistors
R1	390 ohms 1/3 watt 5%
R2	0.47 ohms 2 watt 5%
VR1	4.7k or 5k lin. carbon

Semiconductors
Tr1	BC107
Tr2	BFY51
Tr3	TIP33A
Tr4	BC107
D1 to D4	1N5401 (4 off)

Transformer
T1	Standard mains primary, 15 volt 1.5A. secondary

Switches
S1   D.P.S.T. rotary mains or toggle type
S2   D.P.D.T. toggle type

Miscellaneous
Case, circuit board, control knob, mains lead, wire, solder etc.

Ni-Cad. Charger

Ni-Cad cells are now quite frequently used in battery powered
equipment which has a fairly high current consumption, since
ordinary batteries require frequent replacement in such
applications, and tend to be relatively expensive in the medium
and long term. Ni-Cad cells and a suitable charger are admittedly
more expensive in the short term, even if the charger is home-
constructed at low cost, but this is more than compensated for
by the considerable savings that can be obtained over a longer
period of time.

A special charger is needed for Ni-Cad cells because they have a
very low internal resistance, but must be charged at a fairly low
current in order to avoid damage. In practice this means that
they must be charged from a constant current source. The
circuit shown here (Figure 34) provides a nominal charging
current of 50 mA., and is intended for use with the popular AA
size cells (which are equivalent to HP7 dry cells in size). These
are used in electronic flashguns, cassette recorders, electric toys,
and many other applications. The charger can be used to
charge up to five cells at a time. When charging more than one
cell, the cells should be connected in series across the output,
and not in parallel.

The left hand section of the circuit is the normal form of step-
down isolation, full wave rectifier and smoothing circuit. This
provides a loaded output potential of very roughly 17 volts.

The right hand section of the circuit is the constant current
generator, and is based on a small 5 volt monolithic voltage
regulator. Provided the input voltage is sufficient, the output
terminal of IC1 will, of course, be maintained at a nominal

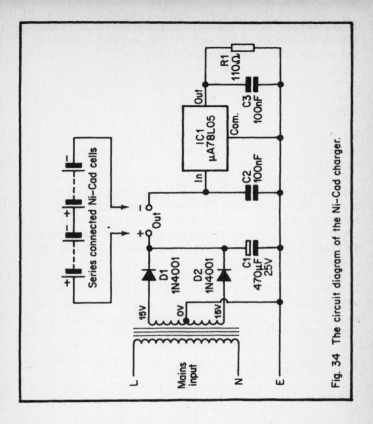

Fig. 34 The circuit diagram of the Ni-Cad charger.

potential of 5 volts above the earth rail. This gives a current of about 45 mA. through R1 which is connected across the output of IC1. The current flowing into the input of IC1 will therefore be approximately 45 mA., plus the current consumed by the regulator i.c. itself, which is just a few mA. and brings the total input current to about 50 mA.

Thus, when a Ni-Cad cell or cells are connected across the output terminals of the circuit, or even if a short circuit is placed across the output terminals, IC1 and its associated circuitry will limit the current flow to only about 50 mA., and an excessive current flow is avoided. There is obviously a limit to the number of cells that can be charged from the unit, since the greater the number of cells connected into circuit, the larger the voltage dropped across them, and the lower the voltage fed to the input of IC1. If too many cells are connected to the unit, the input voltage to IC1 will fall below the minimum level for correct operation (about 7.5 volts), and the Ni-Cads would then receive little or no charge current. Using a component having a secondary rating of 100 mA. in the T1 position it should be possible to charge at least five cells, and six cells can be charged if T1 has a secondary rating of 200 mA. or more.

Plastic battery holders for AA size cells are readily available, and the cells can be fitted into one of these while they are being charged. These battery holders are equipped with a PP3 type connector, and the charger can therefore be fitted with a PP3 battery connector at its output in order to facilitate easy connection to the cells.

The charger can also be used with PP3 size Ni-Cad cells which require a charging current of about 11 mA. T1 needs to have a secondary rating of 100 mA. or more, and R1 should be changed to a 680 ohm component.

Components Ni-Cad Charger (Figure 34)

Resistor
R1   110 ohms 1/3 watt 5%

Capacitors
C1   470 μF 25V
C2, C3   100 nF plastic foil (2 off)

Semiconductors
IC1   78L05 (5 volt, 10 mA. positive regulator)
D1, D2   1N4001 (2 off)

Transformer
T1   Standard mains primary, 15 — 0 — 15 volt 100 or
                200 mA. secondary (see text)

Miscellaneous
Case, circuit board, output connector, mains lead, wire, solder etc.

Electronic Fuse

This simple add-on unit is designed to be connected in the output from a bench power supply, and will cut off the output if a current in excess of some predetermined level is drawn from the supply. It operates extremely rapidly, and is far faster in operation then a conventional fuse. It can also operate at lower currents than is possible with conventional fuses. This unit is ideal for use when experimenting with delicate semiconductor devices which could easily be damaged by an excessive current flow.

The unit will operate on supply voltages of between about 7 and 25 volts, and the trigger current can have any value from a few mA. up to 100 mA. or so. The unit does increase the output impedance of the supply, but this will not be of any serious consequence in the majority of applications. The circuit has a current consumption of about 3.5 mA. at a supply potential of 7 volts, rising to about 12 mA. at a supply voltage of 25 volts (this is in addition to the output current).

Figure 35 shows the circuit diagram of the electronic fuse. Under normal operating conditions Tr1 is biased hard into conduction by the base current it receives through R3, S2, R2 and D1. Power is therefore coupled from the input to the output by way of Rt and Tr1.

If an excessive output current is drawn from the output of the unit, the voltage developed across Rt becomes high enough to switch on Tr3, and a small base current is supplied to Tr3 via R1. Tr3 then supplies a small base current to Tr2, which is biased into conduction and supplies a base current to Tr3. This regenerative action continues until both Tr2 and Tr3 are biased hard into conduction. These two transistors are actually connected to form a sort of highly sensitive thyristor. An ordinary thyristor or s.c.r. is not suitable for use here as it would require a rather high trigger current, and would also tend not to give a latching action at the relatively low operating current used here.

The latching action occurs because once triggered, the

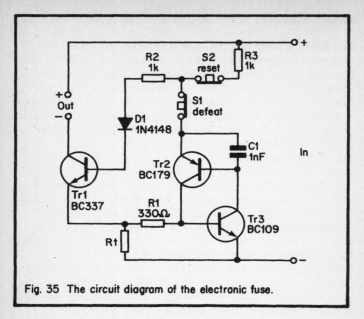

Fig. 35 The circuit diagram of the electronic fuse.

transistors bias each other into conduction and no input bias is needed. Furthermore, even if the current through Rt is reduced to zero, due to the inclusion of R1 neither Tr2 or Tr3 will switch off. R1 and Rt simply act as a collector load resistance for Tr2, and the base voltage of Tr3 remains high enough to keep it conducting heavily.

When Tr2 and Tr3 are triggered, the current through Rt does in fact reduce to zero, because the junction of S1, S2 and R2 is pulled down to only about 1 volt positive of the negative input rail. Due to the inclusion of D1 in the base circuit of Tr1, about 1.2 volts is needed at this point in the circuit in order to bring Tr1 to the threshold of conduction. It therefore ceases to conduct, and cuts off the supply to the output.

Once triggered, the cut-out can be reset by operating S2 momentarily. This cuts the supply of current to Tr2 and Tr3, causing them to switch off. The output is then restored when S2 is released (unless the overload is still present on the output, and the circuit will then immediately retrigger).

One problem with this type of circuit is that the circuit can
tend to be triggered when an item of equipment is initially
connected across the output. This is due to the brief surge of
current taken by the decoupling capacitors in the supplied
equipment. Operating reset button S2 is of no use as the circuit
is simply retriggered each time S2 is released. Defeat switch
S1 has therefore been included. When operated, this simply
disconnects the thyristor circuitry from Tr1's base feed
circuit and the cut-out action is eliminated. This resets the
circuit and gives an opportunity for the decoupling capacitors
in the supplied equipment to charge up. Some caution is
needed before operating S1 though, since both the cut-out and
the supplied equipment could be damaged if this switch is
operated and there is a genuine overload across the output.

C1 is needed merely to prevent spurious operation of the
highly sensitive thyristor circuitry.

The value of Rt must be varied to give the required trigger
current. Its value is equal to 0.5 divided by the required
trigger current in amps (or 500 divided by the required trigger
current in milliamps). In either case the value of Rt is given in
ohms. The answer is unlikely to coincide with a preferred
value, but it is then merely necessary to choose the nearest
preferred value. If, for example, a trigger current of 100 mA.
is required, this gives a calculated value of 5 ohms, and in
practice a 5.1 ohm component would be used, or a 4.7 ohm
type might be a better choice as this is in the E12 series of
preferred values and is more readily available.

Components Electronic Fuse (Figure 35)

Resistors. (All 1/3 watt 5%)
R1   330 ohms
R2   1k
R3   1k
Rt   see text

Capacitor
C1   1 nF ceramic plate

Semiconductors
Tr1   BC337
Tr2   BC179
Tr3   BC109
D1   1N4148

Switches
S1   Push to break, release to make type
S2   Push to break, release to make type

Miscellaneous
Case, circuit board, input and output sockets, wire, solder etc.

Supply Splitter

This device can be used to produce dual balanced supplies
from a single supply, and thus enables operational amplifier
circuits requiring dual rails to be powered from ordinary bench
power supplies. The unit will operate with input voltages of
between 12 and 30 volts (36 volts is the absolute maximum
input voltage), and gives outputs of between + 6 volts and + 15
volts. Output currents of up to about 200 mA. or so can be
comfortably handled by the circuit.

The circuit diagram of the unit is given in Figure 36. The
circuit is based on IC1, which is a Class B power amplifier
device that is really a form of high power operational
amplifier. R1 and R2 form a fairly high impedance centre tap
on the input rails, and IC1 is connected as a unity gain buffer
amplifier which is fed from this centre tap. Half the supply
potential therefore appears at the output of IC1, and this part
of the circuit is at a very low impedance. If this point is made
the OV. rail, the positive and negative input rails then act as
the output rails which are positive and negative respectively to
the central earth rail. Of course, each output rail is at a
potential of only half the input voltage.

C1 to C3 are needed to limit noise level on the output, and to
prevent instability.

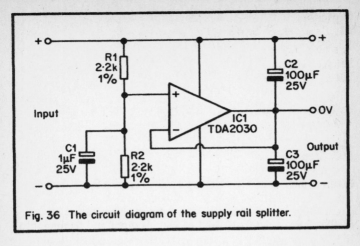

Fig. 36 The circuit diagram of the supply rail splitter.

One problem with this type of circuit is that the OV. rail can only be earthed if the supply has a separate earth socket, and the mains earth is not permanently connected to one or other of the output rails. Many bench supplies have the mains earth connection taken to a separate output socket, so that the appropriate output rail can be earthed, or neither of them are earthed, as circumstances dictate. Another method is to have a 3 way rotary switch which is used to connect the mains earth to negative rail in the first position, the earth socket when in the central position, and the positive rail when in the third position. With either of these two systems, both of which can be applied to the bench power supply designs in this book, there is obviously no problem when using the supply splitter unit. Note that when one of the earthing arrangements mentioned above is used, the chassis and case of the supply must still be permanently connected to the mains earth lead in the interests of safety.

Components Supply Rail Splitter (Figure 36)

Resistors. (All ½ watt 2% or better)
R1   2.2k
R2   2.2k

Capacitors
C1   1 μF 25V
C2, C3   100 μF 25V (2 off)

Semiconductor
IC1   TDA2030

Miscellaneous
Case, circuit board, input and output sockets, wire, solder etc.

D.C. Step-Up

It can sometimes be necessary to power (say) a 9 volt radio
from a 6 volt battery supply, and some form of step up voltage
circuit is then required. One way around this is to use an
oscillator powered from the low voltage input and feeding into
the primary winding of a step-up transformer. The output of
the transformer is then smoothed and rectified to give the
higher d.c. output voltage.

This is not the only method though, and the simple arrangement of Figure 37 can be used where only a modest voltage
step-up is required. IC1 is used in a squarewave oscillator
circuit, providing a low impedance output at a frequency of a
few hundred Hertz. The output signal is coupled by C3 to
a simple smoothing and rectifier circuit consisting of D1, D2
and C4. This circuit produces a positive output with respect
to the positive rail. In a theoretically perfect circuit the voltage
across C4 would be equal to the input voltage, and the voltage
across the output of the unit (which consists of the input
voltage in series with the voltage across C4) would be double
the input voltage. This is not achieved in practice of course, due
to the voltage drop through the rectifiers, and because the peak-
to-peak output voltage swing of IC1 is considerably less than
the input voltage.

From a 6 volt input the prototype produced an output voltage
of about 8 volts or so, and good results were obtained when
powering a 9 volt radio from a 6 volt source via the step-up
circuit. From a 12 volt supply the output is about 18 volts or
so, and an output of 24 volts can be obtained from an input

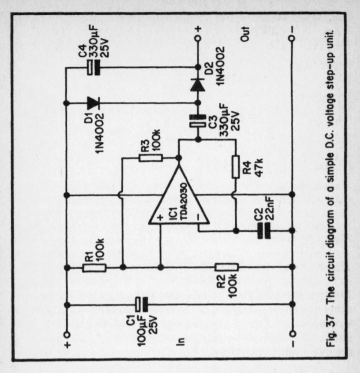

Fig. 37 The circuit diagram of a simple D.C. voltage step—up unit.

potential of about 16 volts. Although the TDA2030 device is not intended to operate from a supply as low as 6 volts, three of these i.c.s were tried in this circuit and all functioned perfectly well with inputs of less than 6 volts.

The maximum current that the unit can supply is well over 100 mA., but it may be necessary to fit IC1 with a small heatsink if the unit is used to continuously supply currents of about 100 mA. or more.

Components D.C. Voltage Step-Up Unit (Figure 37)

Resistors. (All 1/3 watt 5%)
R1   100k

87

R2	100k
R3	100k
R4	47k

Capacitors
C1	100 μF 25V
C2	22 nF plastic foil
C3	330 μF 25V
C4	330 μF 25V

Semiconductors
IC1	TDA2030
D1, D2	1N4002 (2 off)

Miscellaneous
Case, circuit board, input and output sockets, wire solder etc.

Shaver Inverter

This circuit (Figure 38) enables a 240V mains operated shaver to be operated from a 12 volt battery, such as a car or boat battery. It is important to note that it is only capable of supplying a few watts, and is therefore unsuitable for use with virtually any other mains appliance. The circuit consumes about 500 mA. under quiescent conditions, rising to very roughly 1 amp. under load.

The circuit uses IC1 to generate a low impedance squarewave at a frequency of approximately 50 Hertz, and this is then coupled to step-up transformer T1 by way of d.c. blocking capacitor C3. C4 is a filter capacitor which helps to give a better output waveform. The output is not a sinewave, but is adequate for this application.

T1 is an ordinary mains transformer having a secondary voltage of about 4 to 4.5 volts, and a current rating of about 1 to 2 amps. It is, of course, used in reverse so that the required voltage step up is obtained. It may be difficult to obtain a suitable transformer, but surplus component retailers and specialist transformer suppliers should be able to supply a suitable component.

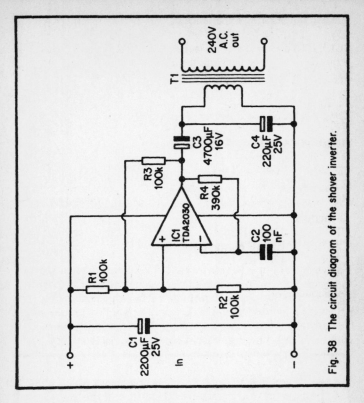

Fig. 38 The circuit diagram of the shaver inverter.

Note that T1 requires a secondary voltage (or primary voltage as it actually is in this case) of about 4 to 4.5 volts, and not 12 volts. This is due to the fact that although the nominal input voltage is 12 volts d.c., and in practice will normally be a little more than this, say typically 13 volts, there is not an output of 12 volts peak-to-peak, which in terms of r.m.s. voltage is about 4.3 volts.

Bear in mind that the output of the unit is at a fairly high voltage, and although it is also at a fairly high impedance and is not as dangerous as the mains supply, it is nevertheless capable of delivering a severe electric shock. The unit should therefore be constructed so that there is no risk of an accidental electric shock being experienced.

IC1 has to dissipate several watts and it must therefore be mounted on a large heatsink having a rating of only about 2 degrees Centigrade per watt or less.

Components Shaver Inverter (Figure 38)

Resistors. (All 1/3 watt 5%)
R1   100k
R2   100k
R3   100k
R4   390k

Capacitors
C1   2200 µF 25V
C2   100 nF plastic foil
C3   4700 µF 16V
C4   220 µF 25V

Semiconductor
IC1   TDA2030

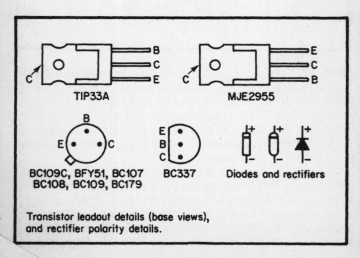

Transistor leadout details (base views),
and rectifier polarity details.

Transformer
T1   see text

Miscellaneous
Case, circuit board, output socket, wire, solder etc.

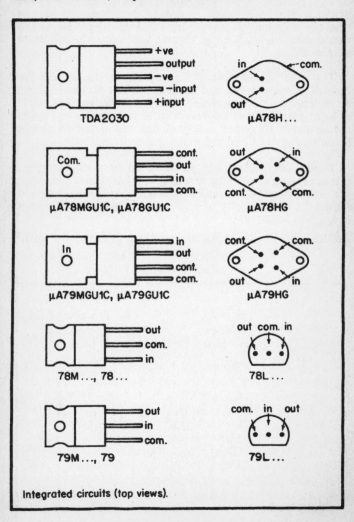

Integrated circuits (top views).

ALSO AVAILABLE

BP192: More Advanced Power Supply Projects.   **£2.95**
R. A. Penfold

This book is the companion volume to BP76 'POWER
SUPPLY PROJECTS' and should be of interest to anyone
who has a reasonable knowledge of power supply basics and
would like to learn about recent developments and more
advanced designs.

The practical and theoretical aspects of the circuits are
covered in some detail, and the reader is not assumed to have
an in-depth knowledge of electronic circuit design. However it
is recommended that anyone who is not familiar with the
fundamentals of power supply design and operation should
consult a copy of BP76 before moving on to this book.

Topics covered include switched mode power supplies,
precision regulators, dual tracking regulators and computer
controlled supplies etc., and it is hoped that this book should
satisfy the vast majority of power supply needs that were not
covered by BP76.

0 85934 166 6   96 pages   178 x 111 mm   1987